Op-Amps –
Their Principles and Applications

Op-Amps –
Their Principles and Applications

J. BRIAN DANCE

Newnes Technical Books

The Butterworth Group

United Kingdom	**Butterworth & Co (Publishers) Ltd** London: 88 Kingsway, WC2B 6AB
Australia	**Butterworths Pty Ltd** Sydney: 586 Pacific Highway, NSW 2067 Also at Melbourne, Brisbane, Adelaide and Perth
Canada	**Butterworth & Co (Canada) Ltd** Toronto: 2265 Midland Avenue, Scarborough, Ontario, M1P 4S1
New Zealand	**Butterworths of New Zealand Ltd** Wellington: T & W Young Building 77—85 Customhouse Quay, 1 CPO Box 472
South Africa	**Butterworth & Co (South Africa) (Pty) Ltd** Durban: 152—154 Gale Street
USA	**Butterworth (Publishers) Inc** Boston: 19 Cummings Park, Woburn, Mass. 01801

First published by Newnes Technical Books 1978
a Butterworth inprint

© J. Brian Dance, 1978

ISBN 0 408 00319 7

British Library Cataloguing in Publication Data

Dance, John Brian
   Op amps.
   1. Operational amplifiers
   I. Title
   621.3815'35   TK7871.58.06

ISBN 0 408 00319 7

Typeset by Butterworths Litho Preparation Department

Printed in England by Billing & Sons Ltd, Guildford, London and Worcester

Preface

Integrated circuit operational amplifiers are one of the most commonly used types of electronic device. When connected to a few external components, they can be used in a very wide variety of applications. This book has been written for non-specialist engineers, home constructors and for anyone who wishes to gain an understanding of operational amplifier circuits and their applications with a minimum of effort.

A non-mathematical and practical approach has been adopted throughout with applications illustrated by practical circuits containing all component values. The principles of operation of all circuits are discussed in detail, but the emphasis is on the practical use of the devices rather than on the internal circuitry used in the amplifiers.

The first three chapters are devoted to circuits using the well-known 741, since this ubiquitous device is so very cheap and can be used for many purposes. Frequency compensation is discussed in Chapter 4 which describes devices requiring external compensating components. Chapter 5 covers devices which have field effect transistors in their input stages. Integrated circuits for audio applications are covered in Chapters 6 and 7 and the book is completed with a glossary of operation amplifier terms.

A wide variety of applications of operational amplifiers will be discussed in this book, but strangely enough no analogue circuits for carrying out mathematical operations have been described. This is because it is felt that such circuits are not likely to be of so much interest to most users as the practical amplifier circuits which have been included. Nevertheless, we should remember that circuits for carrying out mathematical operations gave the name 'operational amplifier' to the devices we shall be discussing.

The material is a modified and updated version of a series of articles which were first published in *Electronics Australia* under the title *'Op-Amps without tears'*. The author would like to acknowledge his gratitude to the Editor of *Electronics Australia*, Mr. J. Rowe, for his help and encouragement with this work and for granting permission for the work to be published in book form.

Acknowledgement is also made to Mr. Keith Stammers of the Physics Department, Birmingham University for reading the manuscript in detail and to various semiconductor manufacturers who have permitted the reproduction of circuits in which their devices are used.

J. Brian Dance

Contents

1
Introduction

The operational amplifier is the most important basic building block of all linear circuits. It has a wide range of applications in such fields as audio power amplifiers, timers, voltage regulators, sensitive measuring circuits, etc.

The basic amplifier

The term 'operational amplifier' was originally applied to high gain amplifiers operating down to zero frequency which were used in analogue computers to perform certain mathematical operations (including addition, subtraction, integration, etc). These high gain amplifiers are now used for a wide variety of applications, but the name 'operational amplifier' or 'op amp' is normally used even though no mathematical operations are involved.

The early operational amplifiers employed discrete components, but it is now much more convenient to employ an integrated circuit. Instead of making up a circuit containing perhaps a hundred discrete components, a small integrated circuit, together with perhaps half a dozen external components, is used. The integrated circuit, or IC, contains a large number of individual components all formed on a miniature silicon chip. All the connections between the internal components are automatically made by photographic techniques during the manufacture of the IC.

One of the main advantages with the use of integrated circuits is the saving in time wiring up numerous connections, but an additional advantage is that the internal connections are much less likely to fail during use than connections made by a soldering iron. Also, a great deal of space and weight can be saved by the use of integrated circuits instead of discrete components.

Another advantage of using integrated circuits is that the cost of most of the commonly used devices is far less than the total cost of the components in an equivalent circuit using discrete components. Indeed,

1

some modern integrated circuits containing many transistors are priced at a value only two or three times the cost of a cheap transistor.

A minor disadvantage of an integrated circuit is that no changes to the internal circuit contained in the device can be made, since the components are fabricated on a monolithic silicon chip which must be carefully sealed against the moisture and other substances in the atmosphere.

Integrated circuit operational amplifiers are best regarded as building blocks which can be used to assemble more complex circuits. These devices are now so convenient to use that very few people even consider the construction of a complete discrete amplifier unless there are special circuit requirements.

The circuit designer is not generally interested in the internal components of an integrated circuit, but only in the performance of the unit as a whole. Therefore, the symbol in Fig. 1 is used to denote

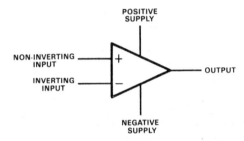

Figure 1 Basic circuit symbol for an operational amplifier

the amplifier. It can be seen that there are two inputs, one output and connections to the positive and negative supply lines.

If the inverting input is made slightly more positive, the output will become more negative; this is why the name 'inverting' is given to this input. If, however, the non-inverting input is made more positive, the output will also become more positive.

The 741

We shall start our discussion with special reference to the 741 device, since it is one of the best known general purpose operational amplifiers and is readily available from almost all of the large semiconductor manufacturers. It is also one of the cheapest of all linear integrated circuits.

2

The user meets only the external circuit, so one of the first questions the newcomer to electronics will ask is 'What does a 741 device look like?'. The device is actually available in a number of different packages, some of which are shown with their connections in Figs. 2–4.

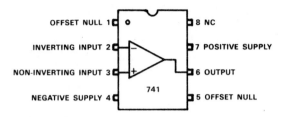

Figure 2 Connections of a 741 device mounted in an 8 pin dual-in-line package

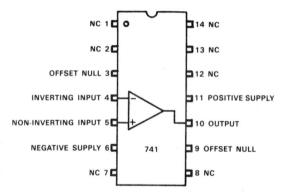

Figure 3 Connections of a 741 device mounted in a 14 pin dual-in-line package

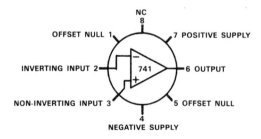

Figure 4 TO-5 circular metal encapsulation with the 741 connections

3

Readers will usually find the type of 741 shown in Fig. 2 the most convenient to use; it is also normally the cheapest. This type of package is known as the 8 pin dual-in-line, since there are four pins on each side of the body of the device and, when viewed from one end, these pins form two lines of four pins per line.

The triangular symbol for an amplifier is drawn on the body of the device in Fig. 2 for clarity. As in all dual-in-line integrated circuits, there is either a small notch between pins 1 and 8 or a small circle near to pin 1 which identifies the end of the device near to pin 1. The user must be careful that the device is used the correct way round and it is only these small marks which provide this information.

An electrically similar 741 device can also be obtained in the 14 pin dual-in-line package shown in Fig. 3. A further type is in the circular metal TO-5 transistor-type package of Fig. 4. Other more expensive packages are available, but the cheapest ones are usually adequate for most of the non-professional requirements.

Sockets

Connections can be soldered either directly to the 741 pins or to a suitable socket and the 741 inserted in the socket. Dual-in-line sockets for the packages shown in Figs. 2 and 3 are readily available, but may cost even more than the device itself. Readers may therefore prefer not to employ a socket, but one should remember that it is much easier to change a device suspected of being faulty if a socket has been used. Sockets are probably more attractive with more expensive devices than the 741. To remove a device from a socket, always slip a screwdriver blade under the body of the device.

Experimenting

One of the best ways of learning about any electronic device is to experiment with it in simple circuits. This is especially true in the case of operational amplifiers. The circuit of Fig. 5 can be used to enable the inexperienced reader to become familiar with the 741 device.

It should be noted that positive and negative power supplies are generally used with the 741. In this circuit ±9 V supplies are shown, since these can easily be attained by using two small batteries. The supplies may be ±15 V if larger output voltages are required but they must never exceed ±18 V with most 741 devices.

The pin connections shown in Fig. 5 are applicable only in the case of the 8 pin dual-in-line device of Fig. 2 or of the circular metal package of Fig. 4. The connections for the 14 pin dual-in-line package are quite different, as shown in Fig. 3. It should be noted that the +9 V supply is fed to pin 7 and the −9 V supply to pin 4. The non-inverting input at pin 3 is conventionally marked '+' and the inverting input at pin 2 '−', but these are *not* the positive and negative power supply connections. The capacitors C1 and C2 may be required to prevent instability if the power supply connections are long, but these capacitors can often be omitted without any troubles arising.

The voltmeter is connected to the output so that one can measure how the output voltage from the 741 varies as the input voltages are changed. This meter should have a full scale deflection of about 10 V, but a centre reading meter (10 V-0-10 V) would be ideal. One can, of course, make a suitable voltmeter by connecting a 100 μA meter in series with a 100 kΩ resistor or a 1 mA meter in series with a 10 kΩ resistor or some similar combination.

Offset nulling

The preset variable resistor VR3 is included to enable the circuit to be trimmed so that the output voltage is zero when the voltage at both of the inputs is zero. This process is known as offset null adjustment.

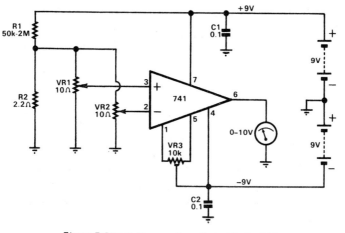

Figure 5 Circuit for experimenting with the 741

Connect both pins 2 and 3 to ground and adjust VR3 for zero output voltage. Note that the adjustment is quite critical. As the device warms up, the output voltage drifts off the zero, but it can be returned to zero by adjusting VR3 again.

This drift of the output voltage with temperature can be important when using the amplifier at high gain. There is no feedback in the Fig. 5 circuit, so the amplifier is operating at maximum gain where the drift with temperature is worst. Indeed, this drift is one of the reasons why operational amplifiers are not normally used in this way.

Gain

The gain of an operational amplifier is generally extremely high, but varies considerably from one device to another. For example, the gain of the 741 at zero frequency is quoted as being typically 200 000 in most manufacturers' data sheets, with a minimum for any one device of 20 000 or 25 000 and no maximum value quoted.

One can make an estimate of the zero frequency gain of a 741 device using the input circuit shown in Fig. 5. The value of R1 should be about 50 kΩ when the 741 has a gain near to the minimum value of 20 000 but a value of 2 MΩ is more suitable for 741 devices which have a high gain. When R1 has a value of 50 kΩ, the potential at the junction of R1 and R2 will be about 400 μV; if this is amplified 20 000 times, a convenient reading of about 8 V on the output meter is optional. If, however, R1 has a value of 2 MΩ, the junction of R1 and R2 will have a potential of about 9 μV; this is suitable for use with a device of a gain of nearly one million to produce a reasonable output voltage reading.

A value of about 500 kΩ may be tried initially for R1. After setting the offset null voltage to zero at the output, leave the inverting input grounded and move VR1 so that the non-inverting input is connected to the potential at the junction of R1 and R2. If the voltage reading at the output is too small to be conveniently read, decrease R1, whilst if the reading is above 7 V, R1 should be increased.

When a suitable value of R1 has been found, note the change in the output voltage reading as the non-inverting input is moved from ground potential to the junction of R1 and R2 by means of VR1, VR2 remaining at ground potential throughout. The voltage gain is equal to this change in output potential divided by the change in the non-inverting input potential, the latter being approximately equal to R2/R1 multiplied by 9 V.

Note that as the potential of the non-inverting input is increased slightly, the output voltage increases, whereas an increase of the inverting input potential will result in a decrease in the output voltage. If the sliders of both VR1 and VR2 are moved from the lowest (ground) potential to the highest potential (at the junction of R1 and R2), the output voltage will show little change, since the increase in potential of the one input is almost exactly balanced by the increase in potential of the other input. Thus the circuit is essentially sensitive to the difference between the potentials of the two inputs.

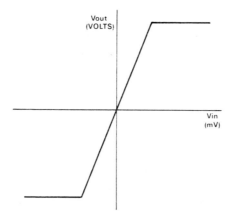

Figure 6 Input/output characteristics of the 741 device

If one keeps the inverting input potential at ground and varies the non-inverting input voltage by VR1, the output voltage varies as shown in Fig. 6. It should be noted that the maximum possible swing of the output voltage is about 1 V less than the potential of either supply line—hence the horizontal parts of the graph of Fig. 6.

AC gain

If an audio signal generator and either an oscilloscope or an AC volt-meter is available, the gain of a 741 device can be measured at various frequencies. A suitable circuit is shown in Fig. 7.

7

The output voltage can be measured by means of an oscilloscope or a suitable AC voltmeter, care being taken that the input is not so high that the output approaches the horizontal parts of the graph in

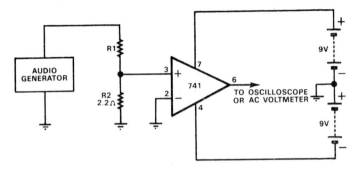

Figure 7 Circuit for measuring the alternating voltage gain of a 741 device

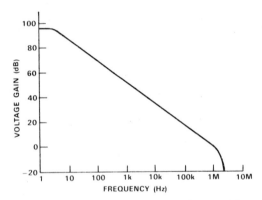

Figure 8 Typical plot of gain versus frequency for a 741 device

Fig. 6. The alternating input voltage is best measured by connecting the oscilloscope or a.c. voltmeter across the audio generator and dividing by the ratio R1/R2.

Thus the gain of the amplifier can be found by simply dividing the alternating output voltage by the alternating input voltage. It will be found that the gain of a 741 device falls off quite rapidly at frequencies above about 5 Hz; this variation of gain with frequency is shown in Fig. 8 for a typical 741 device. It may be noted that the gain falls to zero at a frequency of the order of 1 MHz.

8

The bandwidth of the amplifier is normally taken as the frequency at which the gain has fallen by 3 dB. This is the frequency at which the output voltage has fallen to $1/\sqrt{2}$ or 0.707 of its gain at very low frequencies. The experiment may be repeated with inputs 2 and 3 interchanged in order to check that the gain falls off in a similar way with frequency when the signal is fed to the inverting input.

Feedback

We have seen that the 741 device offers a very high gain at low frequencies. However, this gain varies so much from device to device that we could not even specify definite values of the resistor R1 in Figs. 5 and 7. The gain falls off above about 5 Hz at approximately 20 dB for each factor of ten increase in frequency and the quiescent output voltage varies widely even with small temperature changes.

The reader may well question whether a device with so many disadvantages is likely to be of any practical use. We shall see in the next chapter that the answer to these problems lies in the use of negative feedback. Such feedback does reduce the gain, but it can allow the gain to become dependent only on the values of two external resistors, so that variations from device to device have a negligible effect on the performance. The gain can be made constant up to much higher frequencies than 5 Hz, but it inevitably falls at some value of frequency and continues to fall as the frequency is further increased. The offset voltage still exists, but with a circuit of lower gain the drift of the output voltage becomes tolerable for most applications.

In practice, operational amplifiers are rarely used without negative feedback. The problems we have encountered are just unacceptable in almost all applications. However, we have not wasted our time looking at circuits without feedback, since the understanding we have gained will help us when using the devices. We are now aware of many of their limitations.

The gain we have been measuring is known as the 'open loop' gain, since it is the gain measured with the feedback loop 'open' (that is, with no feedback).

2
Some Basic 741 Circuits

We now consider some practical circuits in which negative feedback is used to stabilise the gain, increase the frequency response, and otherwise improve performance. When a suitable amount of negative feedback is employed, the differences between integrated circuit operational amplifiers of the same type number can be made negligible for all practical purposes.

As the 741 device is a very economical general purpose operational amplifier which is readily available, we will continue to base our circuits on it. However, almost all of the ideas discussed also apply to other operational amplifier devices.

Inverting amplifier

The basic circuit of a 741 inverting amplifier is shown in Fig. 9. The input signal is fed to the inverting input of the 741 via R1 and therefore the output is inverted in sign with respect to the input. For simplicity, the power supply connections are not shown in this circuit, but they must of course be included, as in the circuits discussed in chapter 1. By omitting these connections and the offset nulling circuit, we can concentrate more easily on the parts of the circuit to be discussed.

If there is a small rise in the input potential fed to the resistor R1, this will tend to produce a very small rise in the potential of the inverting input of the 741 (marked '−'), and this results in a fall in the output potential. This fall is fed back through R3 and tends to cancel the rise at the inverting input.

We have already seen that operational amplifiers are designed to have an extremely high gain, so the fall in the output voltage is adequate to almost completely cancel the rise in voltage at the inverting input of the amplifier. It cannot completely cancel the input rise, since a minute change of input potential is needed to produce the output voltage change. However, the inverting input of the 741 remains virtually at earth potential and is therefore usually described as a 'virtual earth' point.

Operational amplifiers are designed to have a very high input impedance. The currents which flow to the inputs of the 741 circuit of Fig. 9 are therefore very small. As the inverting input is virtually at ground potential, the current which flows through R1 is equal to the

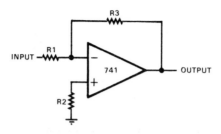

Figure 9 Basic inverting amplifier using the 741; the gain is R3/R1

input voltage, Vi, divided by R1. Similarly, the current flowing through R3 is Vo/R3 where Vo is the output voltage. These two currents are almost equal, since the current flowing to the inverting input is very small indeed.

$$Vi/R1 = Vo/R3$$
hence $Vo/Vi = R3/R1$

But Vo/Vi is equal to the gain of the circuit with feedback. Thus the gain is equal to the ratio of the resistor values R3/R1, and is unaffected by the gain of the amplifier used.

In actual fact this result is only an approximation, since we have assumed that the potential at the inverting input is always zero and this cannot be quite true. Nevertheless, if the gain of the amplifier device itself without feedback is much greater than R3/R1, the gain with feedback is very closely equal to R3/R1.

The input impedance of the circuit of Fig. 9 is almost exactly equal to the resistance of R1, since the one side of this resistor always remains at about earth potential. If one wishes to minimise the effect of small currents flowing into the amplifier inputs, the value of R2 should be approximately equal to the value of R1 in parallel with that of R3.

If a voltage gain of 50 times (34 dB) is required, one may select a value of 50 k for R3 and 1 k for R1. The bandwidth using a typical

741 device will be about 20 kHz at −3 dB down, for this gain. However, the bandwidth is essentially inversely proportional to the gain. Thus one can obtain a gain of 5 for a 200 kHz bandwidth, or a gain of 500 for a 2 kHz bandwidth. The 741 can be used as an audio preamplifier with a gain of up to 50 (or 100 for a more limited frequency response), but special audio preamplifier devices are available which are operational amplifiers with lower noise levels than the 741.

Readers wishing to try this circuit may use two 9 V batteries as the source of power. Alternatively a supply derived from the mains and regulated by a suitable device may be used, but there is no point in applying more than ±15 V and risking damaging the amplifier device.

Non-inverting amplifier

The input voltage is applied to the non-inverting input of the circuit of Fig. 10 and no inversion of the signal waveform therefore occurs. A potential divider, R1 and R2, is included across the output circuit

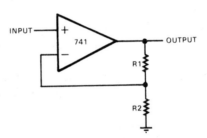

Figure 10 Basic non-inverting amplifier of gain R1/R2 + 1

and the negative feedback signal taken from the junction of these resistors is applied to the inverting input of the 741 device.

If the input potential rises by a small amount Vi, the output voltage will rise by an amount we will call Vo. A fraction of Vo is fed back to the inverting input to provide negative feedback. The potentials at the two inputs rise by almost equal amounts; if this were not so, the difference in potential between these inputs would be multiplied by the very high open loop gain of the 741 device so as to cause a very large change in the output voltage.

12

The voltage across R2 is equal to the fraction R2/(R1 + R2) of Vo. If we assume that the gain of the 741 is so high that the potentials at the two inputs of the device are equal,

$$Vi = Vo\ R2/(R1 + R2)$$

and Gain = Vo/Vi

$$= (R1 + R2)/R2$$

$$= R1/R2 + 1$$

If R1 is much larger than R2, the gain of the circuit is approximately equal to R1/R2, and as before is independent of the particular amplifier in use.

Offset nulling

An offset nulling potentiometer can be used in either of the circuits of Figs. 9 and 10. This involves connecting a potentiometer (perhaps 10 kΩ) between pins 1 and 5 of a standard 8 pin 741 device, with the slider of the potentiometer connected to the negative supply line (see Fig. 5). If feedback resistor values for moderate gain (10 to 100) are selected, the adjustment of the nulling potentiometer is far less critical than when the 741 is used at full gain without any negative feedback.

Indeed, the adjustment of the potentiometer changes the output voltage by only a small fraction of a volt in the Fig. 9 and Fig. 10 circuits at moderate values of gain, whereas in the Fig. 5 circuit a small adjustment of the nulling potentiometer would cause the output to sweep from one extreme to the other. The voltage offset at the input in these circuits is multiplied by the gain of the circuit at zero frequency. Thus in the practical circuits of Figs. 9 and 10, the output potential can be set to zero fairly accurately. It will drift somewhat with temperature, but this drift will be far less than if the 741 is used in the Fig. 5 circuit without feedback.

Buffer amplifier

A simple buffer amplifier having a high input impedance and a low output impedance is shown in Fig. 11. It is essentially similar to the

13

circuit of Fig. 10, but the whole of the output voltage is fed back to the input instead of only a fraction of the output voltage. This type of circuit is known as a voltage follower, since the output voltage follows changes in the input voltage.

In the circuits of Figs. 10 and 11, all of the input current flows into the non-inverting input of the operational amplifier device. The 741 is designed so that this current is quite small and therefore the input impedance of these circuits is much higher than that of Fig. 9 where approximately equal currents flow through R1 and R3.

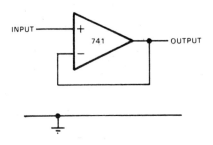

Figure 11 A voltage follower circuit with full negative feedback

The circuit of Fig. 11 is therefore, very useful when a circuit of fairly high input impedance is required, which will not impose an appreciable load on most circuits which are likely to be used to feed it. Apart from the name 'voltage follower', this type of circuit is sometimes called an 'impedance converter', since it converts the high impedance at its input to a relatively low output impedance.

The input impedance of the 741 is typically 1 MΩ with a minimum value of about 0.3 MΩ for any 741 device, whilst the output impedance of the circuit is somewhat less than 1 kΩ.

The circuit of Fig. 11 can be used when no voltage gain is required, whereas the circuits of Figs. 9 and 10 can provide gain. If desired, one of the feedback resistors may be made variable so that the gain can be controlled.

The 100% negative feedback used in the circuit of Fig. 11 renders the input impedance of this circuit especially high. If a circuit of the highest possible input impedance which also has voltage gain is required, an input circuit of the type shown in Fig. 11 may be used with its output driving a circuit similar to Fig. 9 or Fig. 10, since the latter can provide voltage gain. However, in chapter 5 we shall discuss devices

14

which are far more suitable for high input impedance circuits than the 741. A typical circuit which can provide a very wide range of gain values is shown in Fig. 12.

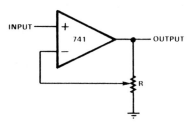

Figure 12 An amplifier of high input impedance whose gain can be varied over a very wide range

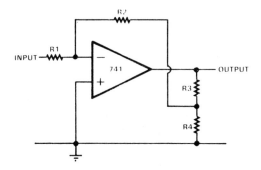

Figure 13 An inverting amplifier which can have a high input impedance and a high gain

Many other variations on the basic operational amplifier circuits are possible. For example, the circuit of Fig. 13 shows how a high gain inverting amplifier can be made with a high input impedance. If the circuit of Fig. 9 is to have a very high gain and the value of R3 is not to be excessively high, R1 must be fairly small and this will result in a relatively low input impedance. However, R1 can be quite large in Fig. 13 even if the gain is to be very high, since R3 and R4 can be chosen so that the fraction of the output voltage fed back is small and R2 does not then need to be especially high.

Sensitive microammeter

The circuit of Fig. 14 shows how a 741 device can be employed to make a sensitive meter with a full scale deflection of 1 microamp. Apart from being a really useful circuit, the inexperienced reader will learn much about the practical use of operational amplifiers by making such simple circuits.

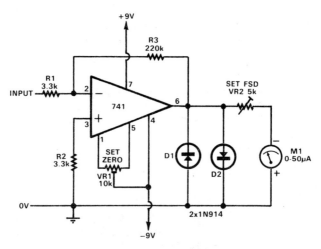

Figure 14 Circuit providing a full scale deflection with an input current of 1 μA. It can also be used as a d.c. millivoltmeter

If an input current flows into the circuit, an almost identical current flows through R3, since the input impedance of the device is high. If the input current if 1 μA, this current flowing through R3 will produce a potential of 0.22 V across this resistor. As pin 2 remains at zero voltage, the 1 μA input current thus produces an output voltage of 0.22 V. If the total resistance of the meter M1 and the variable resistor VR2 is 4.4 kΩ, a current of 50 μA will flow through the meter. Thus the 1 μA input current causes a full scale deflection of the meter.

The diodes D1 and D2 will not pass any appreciable current unless the output voltage exceeds about 0.6 V; in this case one of the diodes will conduct and will prevent the meter from being overloaded and possibly damaged. The equal input resistors R1 and R2 help to reduce drift of the offset voltage.

If the input is positive (that is, if a conventional current flows into the resistor R1), the output will become negative. The positive side of the meter must therefore be grounded and the negative side connected to the 741 output. If desired a 50-0-50 microammeter may be employed, in which case currents of either polarity can be measured with the centre reading meter.

When the meter is to be used, VR1 should first be adjusted so that the meter indicates zero with no input current. A current of 1 μA is then passed into the input. One way of doing this is to connect a 10 V source through a 10 MΩ resistor to the input of the circuit, the negative side of the source being connected to the zero volt line. The 'Set FSD' control VR2 is then adjusted until the meter shows a full scale deflection.

It is also possible to use a 0-100 microammeter in this circuit, but the value of VR2 should then preferably be reduced to about 2.5 kΩ. Other fairly sensitive meters can also be employed, with FSD figures up to about 500 μA, by reducing the value of VR2 to suit.

The input bias current to a typical 741 device is 0.2 μA (maximum value 0.5 μA); it is the average of the two input currents. The input offset current is the difference in the currents to the two inputs when the output is at zero voltage; the input offset current has a typical value of 0.03 μA (maximum 0.2 μA) for the 741 and varies with temperature. Thus errors will occur if an attempt is made to increase the sensitivity of the Fig. 14 circuit by a large factor so as to obtain a full scale deflection with much lower input currents. In due course we shall show how other devices can be used to measure much smaller currents than those for which the Fig. 14 circuit using the 741 is suitable.

The circuit of Fig. 14 can also be used as a voltmeter for measuring steady voltages; VR2 can be adjusted so that the full scale deflection is 200 mV. The power supply and offset nulling circuits shown in Figs. 14 and 15 are also suitable for use in the circuits of Figs. 9 and 13 inclusive.

Multi-range meter

The circuit of Fig. 15 shows the use of a 741 device in a microammeter having several input ranges. When S1 is in position 1, a current of 5 μA flowing through R1, R2 and R3 (total of 200 Ω) will produce 1 mV across these resistors and this can be used to produce a full scale deflection. When S1 is in position 2, 10 μA will then be required to produce a full scale deflection, whilst in position 3 an input current of 20 μA will be required to produce a full scale reading.

The gain of this circuit is approximately 200 (= R6/R4), so 200 mV is available at the output for driving a current of 100 μA through the meter. The adjustment of VR1 is carried out as for the Fig. 14 circuit.

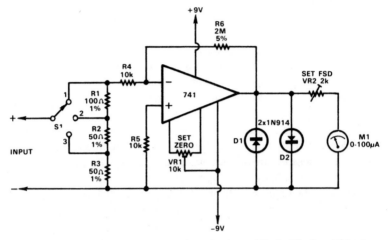

Figure 15 Circuit providing full scale deflections of 5 μA, 10 μA and 20 μA

The correct full scale deflection is set using VR2 on any one of the current ranges and the full scale deflection on the other ranges will then also be correct, since R1, R2 and R3 are close tolerance components.

3
Further 741 Circuits

Audio preamplifier

The 741 (like other operational amplifiers) can be used in many types of circuit.

The circuit of Fig. 16 is that of an audio preamplifier with a high input impedance which is suitable for use with a crystal pick-up, etc. The circuits discussed previously have all employed balanced positive and negative power supply lines so that the 741 can operate correctly when its input and output potentials have values on either side of the zero (earth) potential. In audio applications this is not usually very convenient, since one normally has only a single power supply line in the equipment.

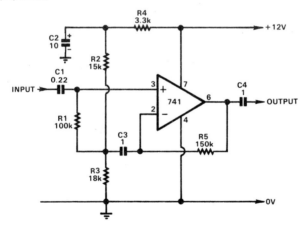

Figure 16 Audio preamplifier using the 741

In the circuit of Fig. 16, R2 and R3 form a potential divider with the value of R4 effectively added to that of R2 at zero frequency. This potential divider effectively maintains the non-inverting input of the 741 at about half the supply line voltage. The output is therefore

19

also kept at about half the supply line voltage, but this is no disadvantage in an audio preamplifier, since C4 prevents the steady component of the output voltage from reaching the following power amplifier. Thus the 741 device can operate correctly as the input and output voltages swing about their mean potential. If the bias were not applied to the non-inverting input, the mean output potential would be low and it would be unable to become appreciably more negative, so the device would not be able to handle negative going signal peaks.

This method of biasing operational amplifiers is often used. Indeed, the next circuit to be discussed uses such bias and it is normally used with most small integrated circuit power amplifiers.

At zero frequency the full output voltage from the 741 device in Fig. 16 is fed back to the inverting input, so the device acts as a voltage follower at this frequency. In other words, the gain is unity at zero frequency and any offset voltage is not multiplied by a high circuit gain. Thus the output potential is kept at about the same potential as that of the non-inverting input and this allows maximum voltage swing on each side of the quiescent output potential.

At audio frequencies, however, the capacitor C3 effectively joins R5 to the junction of R2 and R3. In addition, R3 is effectively in parallel with R2 at audio frequencies, since C2 effectively joins the upper end of R2 to ground as far as audio frequencies are concerned. Thus R5 forms a potential divider with R3 and R2 in parallel and only a portion of the output is fed back to the inverting input at audio frequencies. The gain can be decreased by reducing the value of R5. The lower end of R1 is returned to C3 rather than to ground and this ensures the input impedance is very high.

The reason why the input impedance is high can be understood if one examines the feedback action of the circuit. If the input potential rises for a short time when an alternating voltage is applied to the input, the resulting rise in the output voltage produces a rise in the potential at the junction of R1 and R3 by feedback action. This rise is almost equal to the rise at the input, since the feedback action keeps the two amplifier inputs at almost the same potential. Thus the changes in the potentials at the ends of R1 are almost identical and therefore the alternating current which flows through R1 is very small. As the applied alternating input voltage causes only a very small alternating current in the input circuit, this means that the input impedance is very high.

This type of circuit for obtaining a high input impedance is known as 'bootstrapping', since the potential at the lower end of R1 is pulled up by the input potential or, in other words, 'by its own bootstraps'. The power supply can be of any voltage from about 9 V to 30 V, but 12 V is usually a very convenient value.

Audio mixer

The circuit of Fig. 17 shows an audio mixer unit which produces an output signal which is a combination of the three or more input signals. The 47 kΩ resistors in the input circuits prevent any signal from one input line from reaching any other input.

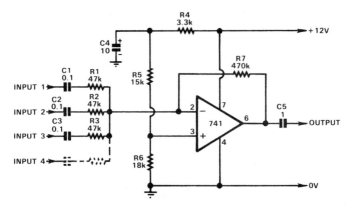

Figure 17 Audio mixer circuit

Biasing of the non-inverting input is again employed in this circuit so as to obviate the need for balanced power supply lines. The gain can be varied over a wide range by altering the value of the 470 kΩ feedback resistor. As in the circuit of Fig. 16, a fairly wide range of power supply voltages can be used.

Variable reference voltage

A simple 741 circuit for providing a variable reference voltage is shown in Fig. 18. The 6.8 V zener is used to provide a reference voltage, since a zener of this voltage can be obtained with a very low temperature coefficient. The current flowing through the zener is constant and is

21

independent of the output load on the 741. The value of R1 should be chosen so that the current passing through D1 allows it to operate at the point of optimum stability.

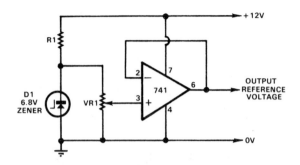

Figure 18 Circuit providing a variable output reference voltage

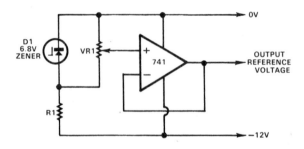

Figure 19 Circuit providing a variable negative reference voltage

The 741 is connected as a voltage follower and provides an output voltage equal to the voltage tapped off by VR1. A similar circuit is shown in Fig. 19 which provides a variable negative output voltage.

Voltage regulator

Integrated circuits especially designed for use as voltage regulators are normally used in this application, but one can nevertheless employ a 741 to make a voltage regulator circuit such as that of Fig. 20.

22

The zener diode in this circuit provides a reference voltage to the 741 device. If the inverting input is momentarily at a potential lower than that of this reference voltage, the output of the 741 will rise in voltage and cause TR1 to conduct more heavily; this will tend to raise the output voltage. After a short time the fraction of the output

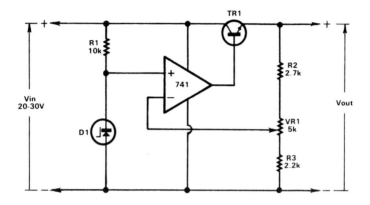

Figure 20 The use of a 741 device in a voltage stabiliser circuit

voltage tapped off by VR1 becomes equal to the reference voltage. The maximum output current depends upon the particular type of transistor used for TR1, but the typical output impedance is less than 0.1 Ω.

It should be noted that the 741 is used as a comparator in this circuit, to compare the reference voltage from the zener diode with that tapped off by VR1.

AC millivoltmeter

It is difficult to make a satisfactory millivoltmeter for alternating signals using a meter and diodes, since the non-linearity of the diode character-istic results in a non-linear scale.

In the circuit of Fig. 21 the input voltage to be measured is fed to a 741 device. The alternating voltage from the output of the 741 drives an alternating current through the diode bridge, through the blocking capacitor C2 and through R2. However, the diode bridge ensures that

23

all current peaks pass through the meter in the same direction. The deflection of the meter is linearly proportional to the alternating input voltage. If the values shown are used, the full scale deflection is about 10 mV.

The output voltage is fed back to the inverting input so as to stabilise the quiescent working point, whilst the alternating voltage developed across R2 is fed back to the non-inverting input and ensures the input impedance exceeds 1 MΩ.

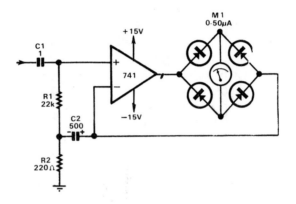

Figure 21 A.C. millivoltmeter with a full scale deflection of 10 mV

The use of the diodes in this feedback network effectively produces a linear response from these non-linear components. Diodes do not readily conduct when only a small voltage is applied across them in the forward direction. In the circuit of Fig. 21, if the non-inverting input becomes slightly more positive, this positive voltage is amplified by a very large factor so that the voltage across the diode bridge is adequate to render the diodes conducting when forward biased. The alternating current passing through the diode bridge develops a voltage across R2 which provides the feedback to the inverting input. Thus the high gain of the 741 effectively cancels the non-linearity of the diodes in the feedback loop.

However, the high frequency response of the circuit of Fig. 21 is limited by the response of the 741 device, so as the frequency rises in the kHz region the deflection produced by a given alternating input voltage will fall.

24

Astable circuit

The circuit of Fig. 22 can be employed to generate square waves with a mark to space ratio of unity. The frequency is dependent mainly on the values of R1 and C1. For example, if C1 is 1000 pF and R1 is 100 Ω, the frequency will be rather less than 10 kHz. The maximum frequency is usually about 20 kHz to 30 kHz.

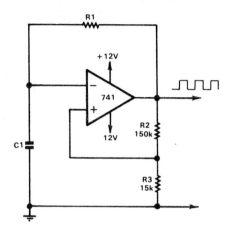

Figure 22 A 741 astable circuit producing symmetrical square waves

Although similar astable circuits can be constructed using two transistors, the 741 astable circuit is very simple and the high gain of the device produces an output waveform with very steep slopes.

The output voltage of a 741 device can swing to within about 80% of the supply voltage lines. Thus the output with ± 12 V supplies is about ± 10 V (20 V peak-to-peak).

If a circuit is required which will produce an unsymmetrical square wave output, one must arrange that the charging and discharging times of the capacitor C1 are unequal. This can be done by replacing the resistor R1 with a parallel circuit, each arm of which contains a resistor in series with a diode, the two diodes pointing in opposite directions. The charging occurs through one diode and resistor, whereas the discharging of C1 takes place by a current passing through the other diode in the opposite direction and through a resistor of different value.

25

Monostable circuits (e.g., for pulse stretching) and bistable circuits can also be made using a 741 device.

Schmitt trigger

A simple Schmitt trigger circuit using the 741 is shown in Fig. 23. When the input voltage increases, a point is reached at which the output voltage changes quite suddenly from its initial 'high' value to a 'low' value. The input voltage must then be reduced well below the point at which switching first occurred before the circuit again switches rapidly back to its original state with the output 'high'.

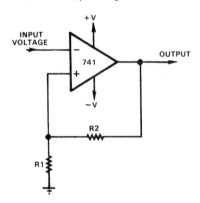

Figure 23 Schmitt trigger circuit

The resistors R2 and R1 form a potential divider and the potential of the non-inverting input will be held at V_{out} times R1/(R1 + R2). Thus as the input voltage increases, switching will occur when it reaches the non-inverting input voltage. The output voltage will now be negative and of the same magnitude as it was previously positive. Thus the input voltage will have to fall to this value before switching back to the original state occurs.

Power supplies

In operational amplifier circuits in which balanced positive and negative power supplies are required, two 9 V batteries will normally be sufficient. However, instability can occur in some cases, especially if the

26

supply leads from the batteries are not very short. It is wise to connect decoupling capacitors of about 0.1 μF from each supply line to ground as near as possible to the integrated circuit; this provides good decoupling at high frequencies. One should avoid the use of batteries which are so old that their internal resistance is high, since this can also lead to instability.

If a mains power supply is to be used, the 0.1 μF decoupling capacitors are still required to ensure stability unless the supply lead lengths between the reservoir capacitor in the power supply unit and the operational amplifier are quite short (less than about 5 cm). Although these 0.1 μF capacitors are in parallel with the much larger electrolytic capacitors in the power supply unit, they provide high frequency decoupling close to the device itself. The power lines are long enough to have an appreciable inductance, and electrolytic capacitors themselves have an appreciable effective inductance in series with their capacitance. Thus the extra decoupling is required to ensure one will not meet troubles through power line coupling.

Similarly, if a single power supply line is to be employed, a single decoupling capacitor (about 0.1 μF) should be connected between this supply line and ground. Mains power supply circuits should preferably be stabilised if one requires long term stability. In addition, stabilisation normally reduces the hum level by a very large factor.

It is often advantageous — especially in experimental work — to use a power supply which cannot deliver a current exceeding some 50 to 150 mA. If an accidental short is made or an incorrect connection during one's experiments, it is then unlikely that enough current will flow from the power supply lines to damage any of the devices being fed with power.

Similar devices

The 741 device is made by most of the large semiconductor manufacturers under type numbers such as LM741 (National Semiconductor), CA741 (RCA), μA741 (Fairchild), MC1741 (Motorola), etc. Although all of these 741 devices should be satisfactory in all of the circuits we have discussed, similar integrated circuits of the same type number from different manufacturers can differ considerably in their electrical behaviour. Most of these differences are negligible with well designed circuits, but it should not be forgotten that they do exist. The manufacturer's data sheet should always be examined in detail, not forgetting the quantities which are not quoted on the data sheet.

There are a number of other operational amplifiers rather like the 741. For example, the 747 device contains two operational amplifiers

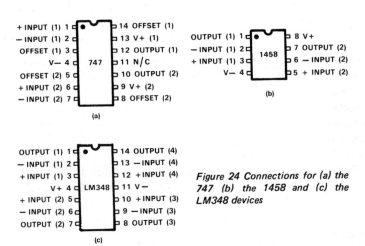

Figure 24 Connections for (a) the 747 (b) the 1458 and (c) the LM348 devices

of the 741 type in a single 14 pin dual-in-line package with the connections of Fig. 24(a). The 1458 device also contains two 741 type devices in a single package, but as this package has 8 connections, there are not enough pins for offset nulling connections to be provided. The connections are shown in Fig. 24(b). The 1458 is also available in a 14 pin dual-in-line case, again without offset nulling connections. Offset nulling can be provided in such devices by applying a bias at an input, but this may not be convenient.

A new device from National Semiconductor, the LM348, has four operational amplifiers similar to the 741 in a single 14 pin dual-in-line package. No offset nulling facilities are provided owing to the limited number of pins available, but the input currents are lower than in the 741 and the supply current to all four amplifiers is less than that to a single conventional 741 device. Such multiple devices are very useful when one requires a circuit in which several operational amplifiers are employed together.

Another device with input currents several times lower than those of the 741 is the 307 device. The connections of the 8 pin dual-in-line package are the same as those of a similar 741 package, but no offset nulling facilities are incorporated.

28

4

Various Integrated Circuit Amplifiers

In the previous chapters of this book we have discussed only circuits based on the 741 device. In this chapter we will first look at some of the other early devices, since this will enable us to understand some important points about integrated circuit operational amplifiers which we have so far omitted for simplicity. We will then consider some of the more recent devices to ascertain in what ways their performance is better than that of the 741.

There is such a proliferation of operational amplifier devices available at present from various manufacturers that it is possible to cover only a small proportion of the vast range. In general, the devices discussed in the following paragraphs are those which are either well known or economical.

Brief history

One of the first monolithic operational amplifiers to become available was the 702, introduced in 1965. This was closely followed by the well-known 709, which was introduced as the μA709 by Fairchild in 1965/66. This provided a much higher gain and increased input impedance, and can be fairly described as the first true operational amplifier integrated circuit to be produced in quantity. The 741 followed in 1968.

The 709

There are various versions of the 709, but the basic electrical characteristics are all very similar. As in the case of the 741, the 709 is normally operated from balanced power supply lines with voltages up to ± 15 V (the absolute maximum permissible value is ± 18 V).

The supply current with ± 15 V lines is typically 2.6 mA (maximum about 7 mA), as opposed to the 1.7 mA typical for the 741. The voltage gain may be rather less than that of the 741, the minimum being 15 000. The input resistance of about 250 kΩ (minimum 50 kΩ) is less than the 1 MΩ of the 741. The 709 input current can be as great as 1500 nA (typical 300 nA) as opposed to the 500 nA (typical 200 nA) of the 741. Thus the characteristics of the 741 are generally slightly better than those of the 709.

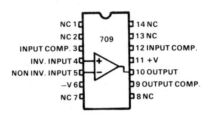

Figure 25 Connections of the 709 14 pin dual-in-line package

When either a 709 or a 741 is operated from ± 15 V supplies, the output voltage can swing over a range of at least ± 12 V (typical ± 14 V), although this range falls by a volt or two at both the positive and negative sides if the load is reduced in value to about 2 kΩ. The maximum positive or negative voltage swing can never exceed the magnitude of the supply line potential, so the maximum output swing decreases as the supply voltage is reduced.

As a rough guide one may assume that the output can swing between ±80% of either supply line voltage. The other 20% of the supply voltage is required to ensure correct operation of the amplifier device circuitry.

The 709 is available in a dual-in-line package with the connections shown in Fig. 25, but can also be obtained in circular metal packages. It can be seen from Fig. 25 that this device has similar non-inverting (+) and inverting (−) inputs to the 741, but there is an absence of offset nulling facilities.

Frequency compensation

As the input frequency to any operational amplifier rises, there will be phase changes between the input and output signals, and at some high

30

frequency this can result in the feedback becoming positive and hence causing oscillation. In the 741 this is prevented by the use of a 30 pF capacitor formed inside the device on the silicon chip, which reduces the gain at high frequencies.

The 709 does not include such an internal capacitor and therefore 'frequency compensating' capacitors must be connected in the external circuit to the 'compensation' terminals. The circuit of a 709 inverting amplifier is shown in Fig. 26 and may be compared with the 741 inverting amplifier of Fig. 9.

The components C1 and R3 provide frequency compensation in the input circuit, whilst C2 provides similar compensation in the output circuit of the 709. The input and output frequency compensation terminals are sometimes labelled 'input lag' and 'output lag' respectively owing to the phase change they produce.

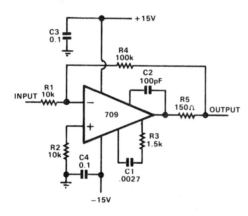

Figure 26 A 709 amplifier with a voltage gain of 10 times

The external compensating capacitors required in 709 circuits complicate the circuits, but there is the advantage that the high frequency response can be altered by a suitable choice of these component values. In particular their optimum values vary with the circuit gain if one requires maximum bandwidth with good stability. If, for example, C1 = 500 pF, R3 = 1.5 kΩ and C2 = 20 pF in Fig. 26, the 709 will provide a bandwidth of about 700 kHz at a gain of 10 with the values of R4 and R1 shown. In contrast the bandwidth of a similar 741 circuit with a gain of 10 is only about 100 kHz.

This difference becomes still more pronounced at higher values of gain. For example, if R4 is increased to 1 MΩ and R1 reduced to 1 kΩ to obtain a voltage gain of 1000, a bandwidth of around 300 kHz can be achieved if R3 = 0, C1 = 10 pF and C2 = 3 pF. This may be compared with the 1 kHz bandwidth of a 741 circuit at a gain of 1000.

Thus, the 709 can give a far greater bandwidth than the 741 when both are operated at high gain, provided that the appropriate values of the frequency compensating components are chosen. However, if the gain of a high gain, large bandwidth 709 circuit is reduced, the values of the compensating capacitors must be increased for stability at high frequencies.

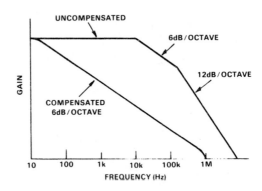

Figure 27 Gain plotted against frequency for compensated devices

Fig. 27 shows how the gain of compensated and uncompensated operational amplifiers varies with frequency. The gain of an uncompensated amplifier starts to fall at 6 dB per octave at a certain frequency, 12 dB per octave at a higher frequency and perhaps 18 dB per octave at a still higher frequency. Compensation involves rolling off the gain from quite low frequencies at a constant 6 dB per octave right up to the point at which the gain is unity.

If the frequency at which the 6 dB per octave compensation roll off commences is fixed at too low a value, this will result in a reduced bandwidth, whilst setting it at too high a frequency will result in oscillation (or at least high frequency peaking and overshoot) when the device is used with the normal negative feedback. If, however, a wide bandwidth is not required, additional stability may be obtained

in the case of poor circuit layouts if the roll off commences at lower
frequencies.

709/741 comparison

As in the case of the 741 circuit of Fig. 9, the voltage gain of the
Fig. 26 circuit is equal to R4/R1, or 10 (20 dB) with the component
values shown. The value of R2 is made approximately equal to the
inverting input circuit impedance in order to minimise the output
offset voltage due to current flow through the input circuit resistors.

The 741 contains circuitry which limits the output current to about
25 mA and no damage will occur if the output is shorted to either
power supply line for an indefinite time. The 709 does not contain
such a protective circuit and if the output is shorted to a supply line or
to ground for a period exceeding a few seconds, the device may be
damaged. The output impedance of the device is about 150 Ω, but an
additional resistor may be included in the output circuit to limit the
output current somewhat in the event of accidental shorting.

The internal circuit of the 741 is designed so that the device will
not 'latch up'. On the other hand, a high or low input voltage applied
to a 709 can cause the output to 'latch up', in which case the output
potential does not return to its normal value when the input voltage
is removed.

The input voltage to a 741 device should always have a value in
between that of the two supply lines with a maximum range of ± 15 V.
The input voltage to a 709 is somewhat more limited, namely a maximum of ± 10, whilst the voltage difference between the two inputs
should not exceed 5 V. The 709 is more likely to oscillate than the 741
if the power supply decoupling capacitors are omitted.

The emitters of the internal output transistors of a 709 are connected
directly together to form the output, whereas bias is applied to the output transistors of a 741 to bring them into Class AB operation. This
reduces crossover distortion, but in any case negative feedback reduces
distortion.

There are minor differences in the specifications of various 709
device types. For example, the typical 709A and 709C input currents
are both 100 nA, but their maximum values are 200 nA and 500 nA
respectively. Similarly, the 709A 'premium' device has a smaller input
offset voltage than the 709C. Various devices like the 709 are available; for example, the MC1437 and MC1537 each consist of two 709-
like devices in a single 14 pin dual-in-line package.

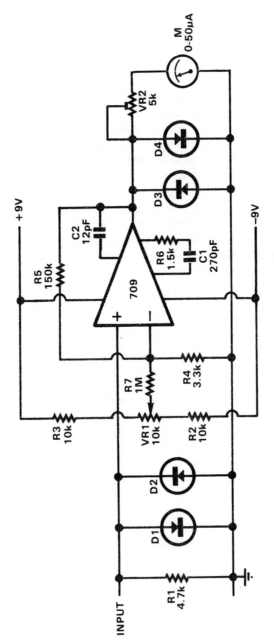

Figure 28 Circuit producing a full scale deflection of 1 µA

34

709 microammeter

The circuit of Fig. 28 shows how a 709 device can be used to produce a full scale deflection of a meter with an input current of 1 µA. The 709 does not have offset nulling facilities and therefore a variable bias must be obtained from VR1 for setting the zero of the meter. The sensitivity is set by VR2.

All of the four diodes in the circuit of Fig. 28 may be 1N914 or 1N4148 silicon types. The diodes D1 and D2 protect the input of the device against any excessive voltage, whilst the diodes D3 and D4 will prevent any excessive voltage being developed across the meter.

An input current of 1 µA flowing through R1 will produce about 4.7 mV at the non-inverting input. The gain of the circuit, R5/R4, is about 45, so the input current produces an output voltage of about 210 mV. This will drive a current of 50 µA through VR2 and the meter when the total resistance of these components is somewhat less than 5 kΩ.

The components R6 and C1 provide input frequency compensation, whilst C2 provides output compensation. Somewhat similar circuits using a 709 device can also be used to make a millivoltmeter, but R1 of Fig. 28 will not normally be used in this case, since a millivoltmeter should normally have a higher impedance than 4.7 kΩ.

The LM101/101A

The LM101 device is designed so that frequency compensation can be effected with a single external capacitor instead of the three components used to provide frequency compensation in the circuits of Figs. 26 and 28. It also incorporates short circuit output protection and will not latch up. It may be regarded as an intermediate device between the 709 and the 741.

The LM101A is like the LM101, but has much lower input currents (typically 30 nA at 25°C, maximum 75 nA) than any of the devices yet discussed. A cheaper version, the LM301A has a typical input current of 70 nA at 25°C (maximum 250 nA), this being three times less than that of a typical 741. The input impedance of an LM301A is typically about twice that of a 741, namely 2 MΩ. The LM307 (mentioned in Chapter 3) has input currents similar to the LM301A, but no external frequency compensating components are needed.

The LM308

The LM108 device developed by National Semiconductor about 1970 employs special transistors, fabricated on the chip, which have a current gain of about 4000. This enables input currents of typically 0.8 nA (maximum 2 nA) to be obtained with an input impedance of about 70 MΩ. A more economical version of this device, the LM308, has input currents of about 1.5 nA (maximum 7 nA) and a typical input resistance of 40 MΩ (minimum 10 MΩ). Thus these devices have input currents well over one hundred times less than that of the 709, whilst the relatively economical LM308 costs about 2½ times that of a 709.

The typical supply current required by the LM108, LM208 and LM308 is only 300 μA (maximum 800 μA), the supply voltage range being ± 2 V to ± 15 V. Thus it is very suitable for battery powered equipment. A single external capacitor is required for frequency compensation with these devices, whilst the gain without feedback is higher than with most of the earlier devices. The common mode rejection ratio (a measure of the ability of the device to ignore "common mode" signals fed to both inputs simultaneously) is also about 10 dB greater than that of a 709 or 741. Unlike the earlier devices, the LM308 has a maximum temperature coefficient of the input offset voltage guaranteed to be no more than 30 μV per degree C.

It should be clear from what has already been said that the LM308 series of devices offers many advantages over the earlier types. In particular, the low input current allows these devices to be used in circuits of very high impedance. The offset voltage of the LM709 device is significantly degraded when the input impedances exceed 10 kΩ, but with the LM101A this is increased to about 500 kΩ, whereas the LM108 operates well with input resistances above 10 megohms.

The effect of high input impedance on the drift of an operational amplifier is well illustrated by Fig. 29 which is reproduced from the National Semi-conductor application note AN-29 *IC Op Amp beats FETs on Input Current.* The performance of the 709 is degraded by input impedances exceeding 3 kΩ, the LM101A by impedances of over 100 kΩ, whilst the LM108 can give good results at 3 MΩ in respect of drift errors.

A variety of types of somewhat similar operational amplifiers with very low input currents are available in which 'super gain' transistors are employed. For example, the LM308A has the same low input current specifications as the LM308, but the input offset voltage is much lower—typically 0.3 mV (maximum 0.5 mV) as against the typical 2 mV (maximum 7 mV) of the LM308. The Motorola MC1456G, MC1456CG and MC1556G are another family of the devices with low input currents, although not quite such low values as the LM308. These Motorola devices are available in T0-99 metal cars, but unlike the LM308 they have offset nulling connections.

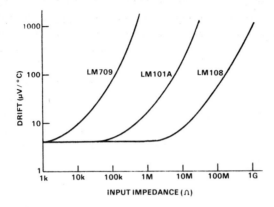

Figure 29 Input drift of various devices plotted against the circuit input impedance

Such high input impedance devices are very useful for amplifying the signals from various types of high impedance transducer, such as piezo-electric ceramic or capacitive types. The low input current of the LM308 enables it to be used in analogue time delay circuits, for delays of up to an hour with a capacitor of only 1 μF in value; this capacitor charges slowly through a resistor and the low input current of the LM308 enables the resistor value to be very high and hence the capacitor to be small for a given time delay.

High impedance amplifier

If an amplifier with an input impedance of 2 MΩ and a gain of 100 is required it might appear that an LM308 used in the general type of circuit shown in Fig. 26 would be suitable. However, the feedback resistor would have to have a value of 200 MΩ for a 2 MΩ input resistor, and such high value resistors are expensive unless wide tolerances are acceptable.

37

The required resistance can be reduced using the type of circuit shown in Fig. 30. The components R4 and R5 form a potential divider so that only one hundredth of the output signal appears across R5. Thus this fraction of the output is fed back through R2 and a gain of 100 is obtained since R1 and R2 are equal. Thus the only high value resistors required are two 2 MΩ components.

The circuit technique used in Fig. 30 does increase the offset voltage by a factor of 200, whereas a conventional circuit with a gain of 100 would increase it by only 101 times. However, if R2 is increased to 20 MΩ and R5 to 5550 Ω, the offset voltage is increased by a factor

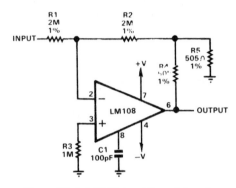

Figure 30 A LM108 amplifier with an input impedance of 2 MΩ and a voltage gain of 100

of 110. Another minor disadvantage of the circuit of Fig. 30 is that the gain is determined by the values of four resistors instead of the normal two; 1% resistor tolerances have been suggested in the circuit of Fig. 30 for fairly close tolerance in the gain.

Frequency compensation in LM308 circuits may be achieved in the normal way by connecting a suitable capacitor between pins 1 and 8; the value of this capacitor may be roughly equal to the output capacitance (30 pF) divided by the closed loop gain. However, the alternative compensation circuit shown in Fig. 30 has the advantage that one obtains a factor of ten improvement in the rejection of power supply noise at the output.

Slew rate

The slew rate of an operational amplifier is a measure of the ability of the device to change its output voltage rapidly when the output signal

38

is large. The 709 and 741 devices have slew rates of about 0.5 V/μs, but much higher slew rates can be obtained using the LM318 (typically 70 V/μs, minimum 50 V/μs). Other more specialised devices can provide slew rates of some hundreds of V/μs.

Slew rate and bandwidth are quite distinct properties. If an amplifier has a large bandwidth, but a small slew rate, it will be able to amplify high frequency signals provided that the output signal level is small. However, when the output signal level increases, the output voltage will not be able to change quickly enough in terms of V/μs for the output signal to be a faithful replica of the input signal.

Micropower devices, etc

Some operational amplifiers are designed to operate from a low supply voltage at very low supply current and are especially useful with battery supplies. Power consumptions of 2 μW at ± 1 V are not uncommon.

5

FET Input Devices

In Chapter 4 we discussed how improvements in the internal circuitry
of operational amplifiers has enabled much lower input currents to be
obtained. However, all of the devices discussed previously employ
bipolar transistors in their input stages. We will now consider the various
types of device which employ field effect transistors in their input stages
so that even lower input currents — down to about 1 pA (one millionth
of a microamp) — can be obtained.

Input current

The input current or 'input bias current' of an operational amplifier is
defined as the average of the two input currents. The 'input offset
current' is the difference between the two input currents. The input
bias current is often of the order of ten times the input offset current,
but this factor can vary widely.

The input current produces a voltage drop across the input resistance
(and in the internal impedance of any signal source feeding the
amplifier) and this causes errors. If the amplifier is operated with equal
resistances in each input circuit, the error is minimised, since it is then
proportional to the difference between the input currents, that is, to
the input offset current.

If an input current of 10 nA is required for the operation of an
amplifier and the external resistance in the input circuit is 200 MΩ, a
voltage drop of 2 V will appear across the resistor and the voltage at
the amplifier input will be 2 V less than expected. Thus the output
voltage error will be 2 V times the amplifier gain.

The importance of reducing the input bias current cannot be empha-
sised too strongly. Indeed, it affects the design of almost all operational
amplifier circuits. For the correct operation of amplifier devices it is
necessary to supply a direct current to each input, this current being
in the range of picoamps to microamps depending on the device type.
Great efforts have been made to reduce input currents and this has led
to the development of new techniques.

FET techniques

The technique of using 'super gain' input transistors (as used in the LM108 series) represents the best which can be achieved with bipolar transistors at the present time. If we wish to make a further substantial reduction of the input current, we must turn to amplifier devices which employ field effect transistors or FETs in their input stages.

One can use discrete FETs which drive a monolithic operational amplifier, but this is generally rather inconvenient when compared with the use of a single integrated device. In addition, the FETs must be specially selected for close matching if a high performance is required; this matching is both troublesome and expensive.

In order to make a device containing the input FETs together with the main amplifier in a single convenient package, the FETs of some devices are integrated on the same silicon chip as the remainder of the amplifier. Unfortunately it has proved most difficult to fabricate well matched, moderately high voltage junction FETs on the same chip as bipolar transistors; such techniques generally result in a low yield of satisfactory devices and hence to a high unit cost.

The resulting devices have typical input offset voltages of 25 to 50 mV, whilst the drift in this offset voltage is of the order of 30 to 50 $\mu V/^\circ C$. If these figures are compared with those for the LM108 (2 mV and 6 $\mu V/^\circ C$) or for the LM108A (0.3 mV and 1 $\mu V/^\circ C$), it is obvious that devices with FETs integrated on the chip have a performance which leaves much to be desired.

This position has now been changed with the release of the National Semiconductor LF155, LF156 and LF157 BiFET devices. These are the first monolithic operational amplifiers with well matched, high voltage junction FETs in the input stage. The input offset voltage has been reduced to about 3 mV and the offset voltage drift is guaranteed not to exceed 5 $\mu V/^\circ C$ in the case of the 'A' devices. In addition, these devices show very low noise.

Another way of achieving the desired characteristics is by the use of the hybrid technique in which an input chip containing two matched FETs is placed in the same package as the main amplifier chip. The latter is a conventional operational amplifier without the input transistors. An excellent performance can be obtained from such devices, but one of the main disadvantages is the relatively high cost of incorporating the two dice in a single package.

Another approach to the problem of obtaining very high input impedance involves the use of MOS (Metal Oxide Semiconductor)

FETs integrated onto the same chip as bipolar transistors. The resulting devices are very economical and the input currents are very low, but their noise performance and temperature drift figures are not so good as those of devices employing junction FETs.

We will now consider some of the devices fabricated by these techniques with some practical circuits.

Discrete FET input

The input impedance of an operational amplifier can be greatly increased if a pair of discrete junction FETs are used as the input to feed a conventional monolithic device, as illustrated in Fig. 31. The two FETs should be a matched pair and are shown connected as source followers; they therefore give a voltage gain of just under unity and the overall gain is almost equal to that of the monolithic device. The FETs act as impedance transformers. No feedback is shown in Fig. 31.

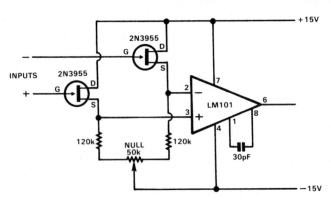

Figure 31 Circuit using discrete FETs to feed an operational amplifier

N-channel junction FETs may be selected for matched characteristics using the simple circuit of Fig. 32. The variable resistor VR1 is reduced in value until the meter indicates a drain current of 200-300 μA. Another FET is now substituted for the original one without altering the setting of the potentiometer. If the drain currents of the two devices are within about 20% of one another, the match is satisfactory for most purposes. The 12 V supply used should have a short circuit current limited to about 50 mA to avoid possible damage to the device

being tested. Cheap plastic encapsulated FETs may not have the low
input current required for this application.

All types of amplifier employing junction FETs in the input stage
can operate with extremely low input currents (a few pA) provided
that the temperature is not too high (not more than about 65°C). The

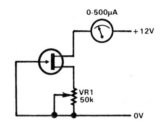

*Figure 32 Circuit for selecting
pairs of FETs for use in the
circuit of Figure 31*

input currents are the reverse leakage currents of the gate-channel
junction diodes and it is a basic property of such diodes that the
reverse current rises exponentially with temperature, roughly doubling
in value for each 10°C rise. At high temperatures (above about 60°C)
lower input currents can be obtained by using the LM108 device.

Monolithic FET devices

Devices which have junction FETs for the input circuit integrated onto
the silicon chip are available with very high input impedances. Their
output characteristics are very similar to those of other conventional
operational amplifiers.

One example of such a monolithic device is the Fairchild μA740C
which has a typical input current of 0.1 nA (maximum 2 nA) at 25°C
and an input offset current of about 60 pA (maximum 300 pA) at the
same temperature. The input resistance is about 10^{12} Ω (one million
MΩ). However, the input offset voltage is typically 30 mV with a
maximum of 110 mV.

The μA740 includes internal frequency compensation, has offset
nulling facilities, will not latch up and includes input and output
protective circuits. It is produced in an 8 pin circular metal package.
The supply current is fairly high at 4.2 mA (maximum 8 mA), whilst
the voltage gain is about one million and the slew rate 6 V/μs. Conventional ± 15 V supplies may be used (maximum ± 22 V).

43

Another FET input monolithic operational amplifier is the Signetics NE536T which has a differential input resistance of about 10^{14} Ω (one hundred million MΩ) at 25°C, the input current being about 30 pA (maximum 100 pA) and the input offset current 5 pA. The input offset voltage is 30 mV (maximum 90 mV) with a typical drift of 30 μV/°C. The NE536T is similar to a conventional operational amplifier in a circular metal case with 8 leads. It has input and output protection, offset nulling facilities and internal compensation. The price is of the order of ten times that of the early bipolar types.

The NE536T may be used in the simple circuit of Fig. 33 as a voltage follower in which it accepts an input of extremely high resistance and provides an output of much lower resistance which can, for example, easily deflect a 1 mA meter. If full advantage is to be taken of the extremely high input impedance of this device, great care must be taken in the construction of the input circuit. The input lead should be soldered onto a stand off insulator employing Teflon (polytetrafluorethylene) as the insulating material and any input terminal must be mounted in a material such as polystyrene—never in metal. Any finger grease near the input terminal may lower the input impedance; the surfaces surrounding the input lead should be washed with industrial ethanol to remove grease without leaving any other deposits.

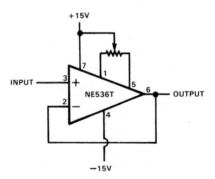

Figure 33 High impedance NE536T voltage follower circuit

The use of sockets should be avoided in high resistance circuits. Guarding of the input connections on any printed circuit board (which must be of high quality glass fibre) by means of a metal guard foil kept at the same potential as the input is very desirable at the highest impedances.

44

What adverse effects are caused by an offset of 30 mV and a drift of 30 μV/$^\circ$C? The offset voltage can be nulled out, but the drift cannot; indeed, offset nulling increases drift. If one uses a device to measure a steady voltage of 1 mV, a drift of 30 μV/$^\circ$C over a 20°C range will produce an input error of 30 $\times$ 20 = 600 μV or 60%. Any amplifier gain will leave the percentage error unchanged. In amplifiers for alternating signals drift may not be quite so serious, but can cause the operating point in the output stage to move into the cut off region; such amplifiers often have a higher gain than those for zero frequency signals.

Hybrid amplifiers

The hybrid or 'monobrid' FET input operational amplifiers are produced in similar types of package to those used for integrated circuits, namely dual-in-line, flatpacks and circular metal packages. The hybrid technique is used to produce a device with a performance which cannot be equalled with purely monolithic devices at the present time. The prices of some hybrid types are little more than that of some monolithic FET types, but precision hybrids are considerably more expensive.

The internal circuits of hybrid devices can employ close tolerance components which cannot be fabricated on monolithic chips. Active laser trimming systems are available which enable the hybrid manufacturer to adjust the device parameters under computer control-at a price.

The National Semiconductor hybrid devices offer a wide range. The type number commence with LH (Linear Hybrid) as opposed to their LM (Linear Monolithic) devices.

One of the most economical hybrids is the LH0042 which consists of a monolithic dual FET input stage internally connected to a compensated monolithic amplifier rather like a 307 device without the input transistors. The input offset current is about 2 pA (maximum 10 pA) at 25°C, whilst the input bias is 15 pA (maximum 50 pA), but these quantities roughly double for each 10°C rise. The input offset voltage is 6 mV (maximum 20 mV) with a 10 μV/$^\circ$C temperature coefficient — appreciably lower than that for monolithic devices. The input impedance is 10^{12} Ω.

The more expensive LH0052 precision FET input operational amplifier is made by laser trimming of the offset. The typical input offset current is thus reduced to 10 fA (0.01 pA) with a maximum of 100 fA for any device at 25°C and the bias to 0.5 pA at the same temperature. The offset voltage is 0.1 mV (maximum 0.5 mV) with a 2μV$^\circ$C (maximum 5 μV/$^\circ$C) temperature coefficient. The input

impedance is about 10^{12} Ω. At low input impedances the LM108
generates less noise than the LH0052, but when the impedance rises
about 150 kΩ, the reverse is true.

Other hybrids use a FET input feeding a fast operational amplifier
like the LM318. For example, the LH0062 high speed FET amplifier
has a 70V/μs slew rate and a 15MHz bandwidth combined with a
0.2 pA input offset current at $25°$C. The LH0063 is even faster with
a 6000 V/μs slew rate and a bandwidth of 100 MHz; the manufacturers
call it a 'damn fast buffer amplifier'. It has a gain of unity, an input
impedance of 10^{10} Ω and can provide 250 mA output current.

Hybrid devices are also used in other fields than operational
amplifiers, but as monolithic manufacturing techniques improve,
many hybrids will be displaced by more economical monolithic devices.

Hybrid circuits

An amplifier which will provide meter readings from inputs in the
picoamp region is shown in Fig. 34. The input current flows through
R1 to the output, very little current flowing into the input of the

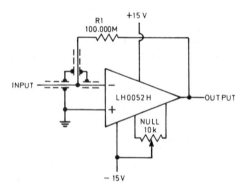

*Figure 34 Picoammeter using the LH0052
hybrid device*

device itself. An input current of 10 pA will produce 1 V across
R1 with the value shown and hence a 1 V change at the output.

The resistor R1 should be a high quality type sealed in glass and
should not be handled before use or finger grease may reduce its
value. The input circuit should be guarded and insulated with Teflon.
The circuit may be converted into a charge sensitive pre-amplifier by
connecting a capacitor across R1.

46

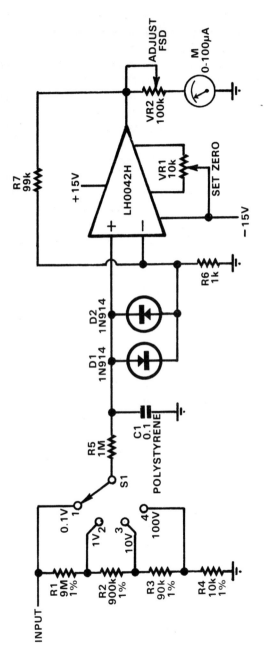

Figure 35 Multirange high impedance voltmeter

47

Voltmeter

The circuit of Fig. 35 shows how a multi-range voltmeter with an input resistance of 10 MΩ can be made using the relatively economical LH0042 hybrid device. No guarding of the input circuit is required, as the resistance is about 10 000 times lower than in Fig. 34. However, it is important that C1 should have a very low leakage current and a polystyrene type should be suitable. D1 and D2 protect the device from excessive input voltages.

When S1 is in position 1, the full input voltage will be applied to the non-inverting input. The gain is (1 + R7/R6) or 100 with the values shown. Thus 0.1 V at the input will produce 10 V at the output. The value of VR2 may be set for the correct full scale deflection and then all of the other ranges will have been calibrated, since 1% tolerance resistors are used in the input circuits. If R6 and R7 are 1% components and a 1% 100 kilohm fixed resistor is substituted for VR2, no calibration is required provided that the resistance of the meter is negligible compared with 100 kΩ.

Wideband AC voltmeter

The circuit of Fig. 36 shows how a high speed FET hybrid device, the LH0062, can be used in a millivoltmeter having ranges from 15 mV upwards which can operate accurately at frequencies from 100 Hz to 500 kHz. The input resistance is 10 MΩ.

The bridge rectifier may consist of four 1N4148 diodes and ensures that the output current always passes through the meter in the same direction. If S1 is set to the 5 V range and a signal with 5 V peaks is applied at the input, the output voltage will rise until the two inputs of the device reach the same potential at any instant. There is a negligible voltage drop across R3, so the current through R9 will be 5/40 mA = 125 μA. The calibration control VR2 is adjusted so that 100 μA passes through the meter when the input is 5 V rms.

BiFET devices

The National Semiconductor LF155 series (LF = Linear FET) was released in 1975 and represents a great development. These devices are

48

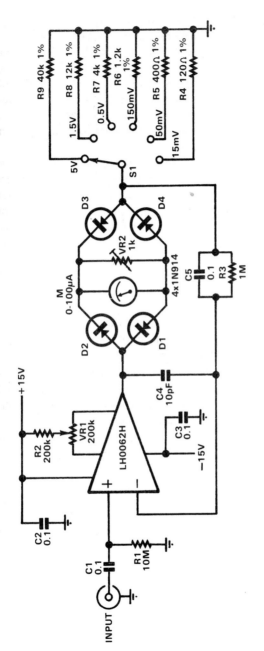

Figure 36 High impedance a.c. millivoltmeter

49

made by ion implantation to achieve very uniform doping across the wafer. They can replace the more expensive hybrid and modular FET operational amplifiers in most applications and have internal compensation.

The series comprises a total of 15 devices. The LF155, 155A, 255, 355 and 355A are for low supply current (2 mA), the LF157 series for wide band uses (slew rate 50 V/μs, gain-bandwidth product 20 MHz) and the LF156 series where a compensated device of moderate speed is required.

When compared with the 741, the LF156 input bias current is 1000 times lower, the slew rate about 100 times greater, the gain-bandwidth product 25 times greater, whilst noise and drift are far lower. The input impedance of 10^{12} ohm is about a million times greater than that of a 741, but the price of the cheapest biFET device is only about two-and-a-half times that of the common 741.

Notch filter

A use of the LF155 may be illustrated by the notch filter circuit of Fig. 37 where the high input resistance of the device enables high value resistors and therefore low value capacitors to be used in the 'twin T' networks. This is important, since close tolerance capacitors of large value are expensive.

The gain of this circuit is constant at unity for all frequencies except those very close to the narrow notch where it falls by about 70 dB.

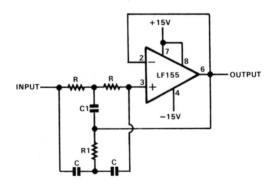

Figure 37 High Q notch filter using the LF155 BiFET device

This frequency is equal to $1/2\pi$ RC where 2R1 = R and 2C = C1. If, for example, R = 10 MΩ and C = 320 pF, the notch will be at the power supply frequency of 50 Hz and unwanted power hum will be rejected by the circuit whilst other frequencies are unaffected. However, hum harmonics are not attenuated.

MOS devices

The RCA Company manufactures three operational amplifiers in which MOS transistors are fabricated on the same chip as bipolar transistors. The first of these devices to be developed was the CA3130 which employs MOS transistors in the input and output stages. The MOS input stage enables an input impedance of 1.5×10^{12} Ω to be obtained, a bipolar intermediate stage provides a high gain and the MOS output stage enables the output voltage to swing within a few millivolts of the potential of either supply line.

The CA3130 has a maximum power supply rating of $\pm$ 8 V (or 16 V with a single supply). However, RCA developed a second type known as the CA3140 which employs a MOS input stage to provide a similar high input impedance, but the maximum power supply voltage rating is $\pm$ 18 V ($\pm$ 22 V in the case of the premium quality CA3140B type). The CA3140 employs internal frequency compensation whereas an external compensating capacitor is required with the CA3130 to prevent instability. The CA3140 has a bipolar output stage and has been designed as replacement for the 741 where one requires a higher input resistance (the CA3140 is nearly one million times better in this respect), far lower input currents, a higher slew rate (9 V /μs as against 0.5 V/μs for the 741) and a gain-bandwidth product of 4.5 MHz rather than the 1 MHz of the 741. The large signal voltage gain of the CA3140 is similar to that of the 741, but the typical input offset voltage of 5 mV (maximum 15 mV) is greater than that of the 741 which is typically 2 mV (maximum 6 mV).

The third type of operational amplifier with MOS input transistors is the CA3160 which is similar to the CA3130 except that it has internal frequency compensation, so no external compensating capacitor is required. The price of all of the three types of RCA MOS devices is of the order of two to three times the price of a normal 741 device, but the premium types with a suffix A or B are more expensive. The types with the suffix 'T' (such as the CA3130T) have straight leads, whereas the 'S' types have their leads bent so that they are in the dual-in-line configuration. Dual-in-line versions of the CA3130 and CA3140 are also being made available, whilst the CA3440 will be a quad version of the CA3140.

Applications

The applications of the CA3130, CA3140 and CA3160 are very numerous, typical examples being given in the data sheets for these devices. They are very useful in impedance converter circuits (voltage followers) of the general type shown in Figs. 11 and 33, but the CA3130 device requires a compensating capacitor between pins 1 and 8 (about 100 pF). The high input impedance of these devices renders them very suitable for use in tone control circuits, function generators in which the frequency can be varied over a range of 10^6 :1 by the use of a single control, etc. The high input resistance enables resistors of very large value to be employed and therefore one can obtain large time constants with relatively small values of capacitors.

It is interesting to note that the CA3160 data sheets include a circuit using a CA3160 device feeding a CA3140 (with feedback across the whole circuit) to provide full scale deflections with input currents of ± 3 pA on a 500-0-500 μA meter. However, we will consider a simpler multi-range meter circuit.

An economical meter

The CA3140 may be used in the type of circuit shown in Fig. 38 to measure steady voltages or currents. When S1 is in position 1, the gain is 100, so an input of 10 mV will produce 1 V at the output and this will give a full scale meter deflection. The other scales shown are 30 mV, 100 mV, 300 mV and 1 V, the input impedance on all ranges being 10 megohms (corresponding to 10^9 to 10^7 ohms/volt). C1R2 filter any high frequencies from the input, whilst VR1 sets the zero.

This circuit may also be used to measure small currents. For example, with S1 in position 1, the full scale deflection with 10 mV at the input will be obtained when 1 nA flows through R1, the other ranges being 3 nA, 10 nA, 30 nA and 100 nA. If R1 is shunted by a 100 kΩ resistor, the current ranges will be 100 nA to 10 μA.

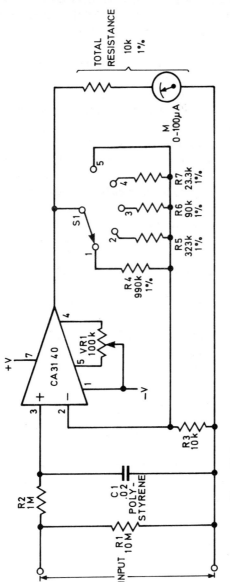

Figure 38 Economical multimeter with full scale deflections down to 10 mV and 1 nA

53

The CA3140 input current is typically 5 pA (maximum 50 pA for any CA3140) and this will flow through R2 producing 5 μV (maximum 50 μV) across it. Thus the error on the 10 mV range due to this is 0.05% typical or 0.5% maximum. However, if one is measuring current, the current passing through R1 differs from the input current by the input bias current of the CA3140. At an input current of 1 nA, the error due to this is 0.5% typical (5% maximum). Nevertheless, this economical circuit is most useful. It may be used (without M and its series resistor) with any standard moving coil multimeter set to the 1 V range to greatly increase the sensitivity of the multimeter. Equally important for many applications is the great increase in input impedance one obtains over that of a normal moving coil voltmeter.

6
Audio Power Circuits

In the previous chapters we have discussed normal operational amplifiers, which can provide output currents of the order of 20 mA. Such currents are too small to operate a loudspeaker at an appreciable volume. It is possible to use the output from such a device to feed a pair of complementary power transistors operating as emitter followers in Class B. These amplify the current sufficiently to drive a loudspeaker.

However, it is normally far more convenient to employ one of the special types of operational amplifier which contain internal transistors capable of handling much higher currents than those obtainable from ordinary operational amplifiers. Such power devices can drive a loudspeaker directly, or deliver power to another type of load.

In many of these devices inverting and non-inverting inputs are available, as in an operational amplifier, but in other types of power amplifier only one of the inputs has an external connection.

Power output

The maximum output power which a device can deliver into a load is determined by the maximum voltage swing at the output of the device and the maximum current which the output can deliver to the load. These quantities are determined by the design of the output transistors inside the device, since there is a maximum voltage which can safely be applied to any transistor and a maximum current which can be allowed to flow through it.

Let us consider the case of a device which can provide output voltage swings of $\pm$ 12 V and a maximum current of 3 A. Obviously the device must be operated from balanced positive and negative power supply lines in order to obtain the $\pm$ 12 V output swing, the voltage of each supply line being numerically a few volts greater than 12 V (typically about $\pm$ 16 V); the extra few volts are required for the correct operation of the device and do not appear across the load.

The device under discussion will deliver the maximum current of 3 A into a load impedance of $12/3 = 4 \ \Omega$. The peak power delivered will be 12 X 3 = 36 W, but amplifiers are almost always rated on their rms power output which is one half of the peak power, namely 18 W in this case.

If such a device is connected across a load of impedance less than 4 Ω, the output current will tend to rise to a value above the maximum permissible 3 A. In some devices this will cause damage; such damage may occur if the loudspeaker leads are accidentally shorted together when an input signal is applied. However most of the modern devices designed to deliver a moderate amount of power have an internal current limiting circuit, built onto the silicon chip, which prevents the output current rising above the maximum permissible value for the device concerned.

Power devices can be operated at less than their maximum permissible voltage, but the maximum power which can be obtained from the device will then be greatly reduced. The output of a typical device which can deliver 2 W when operated from a 12 V supply will fall to about 0.1 W when the supply voltage falls to 4 V. Some devices will not even operate correctly at supply voltages as low as 4 V.

Most power integrated circuits provide a fairly low output power (a maximum of a few watts) and are operated from a single power supply. However, the devices which can supply the maximum power yet obtainable from monolithic devices (about 20 W) are usually operated from balanced positive and negative supplies. The quiescent output voltage is then zero, so that no output capacitor is required in series with the loudspeaker to prevent a steady current from flowing through the voice coil. Such a current would displace the coil from its normal position and would reduce the undistorted output power or prevent correct operation.

The mean output potential of devices operating from a single supply is about half the supply voltage with respect to earth. A large electrolytic capacitor must therefore be connected in the output circuit to prevent any steady current from flowing through the loudspeaker. The value of this capacitor must be large enough to enable the required bass response to be obtained.

It follows from the previous discussion that the maximum rms power output from an amplifier is $V^2/2R$ where $\pm$ V is the maximum output voltage swing and R is the load impedance. When a single power supply is used, however, the output power is $V^2/8R$ where V is the peak-to-peak output voltage swing; V is a few volts less than the power supply voltage.

Monolithic audio amplifier devices are very easy to use provided one takes reasonable precautions to keep the input and output connections well separated to prevent feedback and possible oscillation. The use of such devices greatly simplifies the task of making an amplifier which will provide low to medium output levels. Audio amplifier devices are often the first type of integrated circuit used by a newcomer to electronics, and are ideal for the home constructor.

In general the writer would advise the inexperienced person *not* to employ a socket with any devices of moderate or high power output, especially if they are operated at a high gain, since the use of a socket can greatly increase stray capacitance and hence the probability of oscillation. In addition, the use of a socket with some types of integrated circuit audio amplifier can increase the thermal resistance to the surrounding air, and this results in the device operating at a higher temperature.

The devices available include very low power types providing a maximum audio output signal of a fraction of a watt, a number of economical devices with a maximum output of about 2 W which are usually designed to operate from quite low supply voltages, quite a large number of medium power devices providing outputs of the order of 6 W, and a few 20 W devices.

Some characteristics of various modern power devices will now be discussed together with some typical circuits. In addition, we will consider a few devices which contain two separate audio amplifiers in a single package; these devices are very useful when constructing a small stereo amplifier in which a single device provides power to both of the loudspeakers.

Another type of device especially designed for television sound systems incorporates an audio power amplifier in the same package as a sound IF amplifier and a volume control circuit.

The LM380N

The National Semiconductor LM380N can be employed in circuits with very few additional components, such as that shown in Fig. 39. It can deliver about 2.5 W into an 8 Ω load when operated from an 18 V supply.

The input to the Fig. 39 circuit is fed to the non-inverting input, but it can be taken to the inverting input instead. The capacitor C1 is the output blocking capacitor discussed previously; a somewhat smaller value may be used if a limited bass response is acceptable. The optional components R1 and C2 form a so-called 'Zobel' network which may help to prevent possible instability at high frequencies (5-10 MHz) when certain types of reactive load are used.

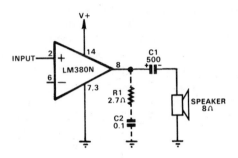

Figure 39 Simple LM380N power amplifier circuit. The inverting input is not connected

The quiescent current consumption of the LM380N is about 7 mA. An internal current limiting circuit is incorporated into the device which limits the output current to 1.3 A if, for example, the output leads are accidentally shorted. Another internal circuit switches off the power in the device when the temperature of the chip approaches the maximum safe value.

The voltage gain of the LM380N is fixed at 50 times (34 dB) by the values of the internal resistors used. This enables the simplest possible external circuit to be employed, but renders the device somewhat less versatile than those devices in which the gain is determined by the values of external resistors. Internal frequency compensation is also incorporated onto the chip.

If the power supply capacitor is more than about 5 cm from the device, a 0.1 μF capacitor should be soldered directly across the power supply connections to the device to reduce the possibility of instability due to supply lead inductance. A capacitor of about 5 μF connected between pin 1 and ground will provide about 38 dB of rejection of ripple (that is, hum) on the power supply line.

An LM380N circuit for use with a crystal pick-up is shown in Fig. 40. As the value of the volume control R2 is reduced, the input signal is applied to both inputs and this common mode input signal produces less output. The control R2 and internal 150 kΩ resistor from pin 6 to earth act as a potential divider for the input signal. This type of circuit provides a much higher input impedance than the normal potential divider type of volume control. The treble control shown reduces the gain at high frequencies by allowing the high frequencies to pass through R1 and the small capacitor C1 to the inverting input where it effectively opposes the signal to the non-inverting input.

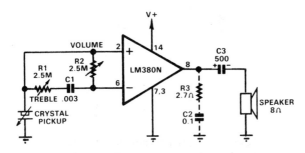

Figure 40 Crystal pick-up amplifier circuit with volume and treble controls

More power can be obtained (about 5 W) by using two LM380N devices in a bridge or push-pull circuit. The loudspeaker is connected between the two outputs and the input signal is fed to the non-inverting input of one of the devices and to the inverting input of the other devices.

The LM380N is normally supplied as a 14 pin dual-in-line integrated circuit, but is also available in an 8 pin dual-in-line package with different connections from those shown in the circuits. The LM384 is a higher voltage version of the LM380N, the absolute maximum permissible voltage being 28 V as opposed to the 22 V of the LM380N. The LM384 can deliver at least 5 W into an 8 Ω load at a total harmonic distortion of 10% using a 22 V supply; a heat sink should be used. The ULN-2280 is a similar device to the LM380N, but is manufactured by Sprague.

Low voltage devices

The very economical TBA820 device from SGS-ATES has been designed so that it can be used with supplies as low as 3 V, although the absolute maximum supply is 16 V. It will deliver 2 W into an 8 Ω load with a 12 V supply or 1.2 W into 8 Ω from a 9 V supply. The quiescent current is 4 mA, whilst the maximum permissible output current is 1.5 A.

A typical TBA820 circuit is shown in Fig. 41. The gain is determined by the ratio of an internal 6 kΩ feedback resistor to the value of R2; the latter may be varied from about 10 to 120 Ω so as to vary the gain

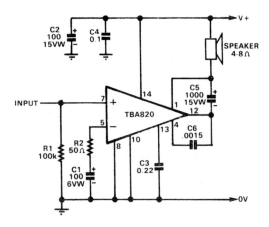

Figure 41 TBA820 audio amplifier

from 750 (55 dB) to 50 (34 dB). The gain is about 42 dB with the value shown. The capacitor C6 provides frequency compensation and may be varied to obtain the required bandwidth, but the value required varies with the gain. For example, if R2 is 100 Ω and C6 is 200 pF the bandwidth is about 20 kHz, but is reduced to about 5 kHz when C6 is increased to 1200 pF. Similarly, if R2 is 50 Ω and C6 is 1800 pF, the bandwidth is about 10 kHz.

A capacitor of about 50 µF connected between pin 2 and the positive line will provide about 42 dB of ripple rejection if the power supply line is not well smoothed and will also tend to prevent the possibility of low frequency oscillation ('motorboating') in battery powered equipment when the internal resistance of the battery rises with age.

The LM386N

The LM386N is another power amplifier designed to operate from low voltages, namely 4 V to 15 V, at a quiescent current of only 3 mA. The gain is internally set to 20 (26 dB) by internal resistor values, but an extra resistor and capacitor can be used to increase the gain up to any value up to 200 (46 dB). In Fig. 42 this capacitor is used without any series resistor to obtain a gain of 200. The components R2 and C3 form the normal Zobel network.

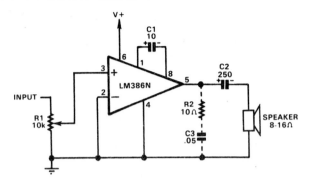

Figure 42 Simple low voltage amplifier using the LM386N

The LM386N is supplied in an 8 pin dual-in-line package. It can provide an output of about 500 mW at 10% total harmonic distortion into a 16 Ω load when fed from a 9 V supply.

Economical devices with even lower rated outputs are available, such as the very cheap Motorola MFC4000B device designed to deliver 0.25 W into 16 Ω with a 9 V supply and the MC1306P 0.5W device.

Medium power devices

One of the best known medium power devices is the TBA810 which can deliver 7 W into 4 Ω when fed from a 16 V supply, or 6 W into 4 Ω from a 14.4 V supply. The maximum supply voltage is 20 V and the maximum output current 2.5 A. A thermal shut-down circuit is incorporated into this device to prevent damage from overheating and to reduce the size of the heat sink required.

The TBA810 has a quad-in-line configuration, but the centre pins on each side have been replaced by cooling fins. The TBA810S version has these fins bent downwards so that they can be soldered to the copper foil of a printed circuit board for cooling; this is known as the FINDIP package. The TBA810AS is similar, but has short fins with holes to which small heat sinks can be bolted.

61

A typical TBA810 circuit is shown in Fig. 43; it is rather like the TBA820 circuit of Fig. 41. The gain is about 80 with the value of R2 shown. C4 and C5 control the bandwidth, which is about 12 kHz with

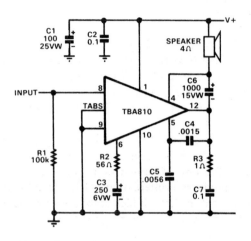

Figure 43 A 7 W amplifier using the TBA810S or the TBA810AS

the values shown. As in the case of the TBA820, it is essential to employ a resistor R1 between the input and ground or the device will not operate; the LM380N has an internal 150 k resistor from the input to ground, so an external resistor is not usually required with this device.

The TCA830S is a device rather similar to the TBA810S in a FINDIP package, but the maximum output current is 2 A. It can deliver a 4.2 W into a 4 Ω load when fed from a 14 V supply. The TBA800 is another FINDIP device which can operate at a higher voltage (maximum 30 V) but which can deliver only 1.5A. Thus it is used with higher impedance loads and can deliver 5 W into 16 Ω using a 24 V aupply.

The TCA940 can provide 10 W into 4 Ω using a 20 V supply and incorporates both thermal overload and output current limiting circuits. This device has short tabs for the attachment of a heat sink, but the TCA940E is a similar device in a FINDIP package which can deliver 6.5 W into 8 Ω from a 20 V supply.

Another medium power device, the SN70008N from Texas Instruments, can deliver 10 W into a 4 Ω load from a 20 V supply. One of its most interesting features is the use of a flat plastic body with a hole for bolting a metal insert to a heat sink. Constructors not using a printed circuit board may find this type of encapsulation more convenient than dual-in-line packages.

20 W devices

The TDA2020 from SGS-ATES was the first monolithic power device capable of delivering 20 W continuously into 4 Ω at 1% total harmonic distortion when fed from ± 18 V lines. It is supplied in a 14 pin quad or dual-in-line package with a copper insert for clamping to a heat sink. The TDA2010 is a lower voltage version of the TDA2020 with a 12 W power rating.

Both thermal shut-down and output current limiting are incorporated into these devices. The current limiting circuits in these devices are most ingenious. The flow of current through a gold bonding wire (about 30 mΩ) produces a voltage drop which is used to monitor the output current and if the latter is high at the same time as the voltage across the output transistor is high, the base drive current is diverted from the output stage.

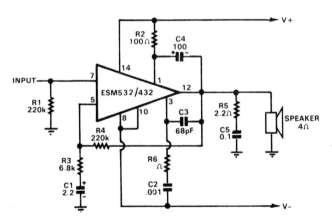

Figure 44 Amplifier for outputs of about 20 W using balanced power supplies

Two rather similar 20 W devices have been produced by Thomson-CSF of France. The ESM532 is rated for a maximum supply of ± 18 V and the ESM432 for a maximum of ± 15 V. Both devices can deliver up to 3.5 A and have current limiting and thermal overload circuits.

63

They are encapsulated in 14 pin quad-in-line packages with a copper slug along the back for clamping to a heat sink. Similar devices with an 'N' suffix have a bracket fitted to the copper slug.

A typical circuit for the ESM532 or ESM432 is shown in Fig. 44 using balanced supply lines so that no output capacitor is required in series with the loudspeaker. The supply voltage may be ± 15 V or rather lower for the ESM432 to allow a margin of safety. The gain is approximately R4/R3, whilst C2 and C3 provide frequency compensation. The 'bootstrap' components R2 and C4 may be omitted if pin 1 is connected directly to the positive line, but the output power will then fall more quickly with the supply voltage on load.

The ESM432 and ESM532 devices can also be used for vertical sweep circuits in television receivers.

Dual power devices

The National Semiconductor LM377, LM378 and LM379 are dual power amplifiers intended mainly for stereo use. Their respective power outputs and maximum permissible operating voltages are shown in Table 1.

Table 1. Power capabilities of dual devices

Type no.	Max. power per amplifier	Load (ohms)	Max. supply voltage	Max. power in bridge circuit, W
LM377	2 W	8/16	26	4
LM378	4 W	8/16	35	8
LM379	7 W	8	35	13

The outputs shown in the last column are obtainable when the two amplifiers of one of these devices are operated as a single push-pull amplifier. The input signal is connected to the inverting input of one of the amplifiers and to the non-inverting input of the other, the loudspeaker being connected directly between the two outputs.

A basic stereo amplifier circuit using one of these devices is shown in Fig. 45. Input capacitors must be employed so that a bias voltage can be applied from the bias pin through R3 and R4 to both inputs; this bias ensures that the mean output potential is kept at about half the supply voltage. The gain of each amplifier can be separately adjusted and is approximately equal to R6/R1 or R7/R5. The devices incorporate internal frequency compensation, thermal overload and current limiting circuitry.

The LM377 and LM378 are supplied in standard 14 pin dual-in-line packages, but the more recently released LM379 is supplied in a special

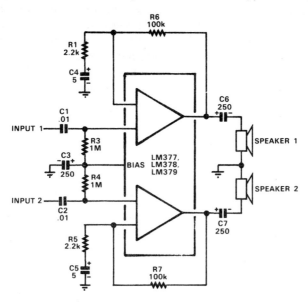

Figure 45 Stereo amplifier circuit using a single dual power device

16 pin dual-in-line package with especially wide spacing between the two rows of pins and a metal insert for bolting to an external heat sink. The electrical circuit of all of these types is similar, whilst the Sprague ULN-2274 is similar to the LM377 and the ULN-2278 similar to the LM378.

General conclusions

The maximum power which can be obtained from a single monolithic audio amplifier device is, at present, about 20 W, but work is being carried out on a higher power device for outputs of at least 50 W and these should become available when the manufacturers are satisfied that there is an adequate market. European manufacturers are well ahead of the US companies in power device development.

The output from two 20 W devices in a bridge circuit can reach about 36 W, but higher power levels involve the use of either discrete or hybrid circuits. Output current limiting circuits are easily incorporated in all types of amplifier, but thermal protection is most readily applied to monolithic devices where all of the transistors are on the same chip. In discrete or hybrid circuits power transistors could be destroyed by heat before that heat raised the temperature of the sensing circuit which could limit the output current. On the other hand, the problems associated with thermal feedback (which can lead to distortion at low frequencies) cause problems to the power integrated circuit designer, but are not so vital in discrete or hybrid circuits.

7
Low Noise Audio Preamplifiers

Standard operational amplifiers can be employed as audio preamplifiers; indeed, we have already described such a circuit in Chapter 3 (Fig. 16) using the 741 device. However, the low level signals provided by magnetic tape replay heads, high quality record player cartridges, high quality microphones, etc. require amplifiers which produce less noise than a standard operational amplifier if one is to obtain the maximum signal to noise ratio.

A number of low noise amplifiers especially designed for audio and other applications are available. They have the advantages over the standard types of operational amplifier of lower noise due to the internal circuitry of the devices, better rejection of any hum or noise on the power supply lines, whilst the bandwidth and gain are usually greater than those of an economical general purpose operational amplifier.

In many cases, the device manufacturers have incorporated two low noise amplifiers in a single package so that the one device can amplify both of the signals in the two channels of a stereo system.

The LM381N

The National Semiconductor LM381N device is one of the best known dual low noise amplifiers. It has an open loop gain of over 100 dB and a power bandwidth of 75 kHz at the 20 V peak-to-peak level. An internal frequency compensating capacitor provides stable operation with voltage gains of 10 or more, but an additional external capacitor should be employed at lower values of gain. The LM381A is a special version of the LM381 for use in very low noise systems, such as for amplifying the signals from hydrophones or in studio tape recorders, etc.

A typical tape playback amplifier using the LM381 is shown in Fig. 46. The tape head provides an output of rather less than 1 mV at 1 kHz and this is amplified to a level of about 0.5 V at the output. In addition, the feedback network provides the standard NAB (National Association of Broadcasters) response at different frequencies; the gain falls with frequency by about 30 dB between about 50 Hz and

3 kHz. High frequencies pass more easily through C3 in the feedback network than low frequency signals and therefore the amount of negative feedback increases with frequency, whilst the gain decreases. This enables the overall record/replay characteristic to be kept fairly 'flat' over the whole of the audio range. Only one channel is shown in Fig. 46, the other half of the same device being connected in a similar circuit for use in the other stereo channel.

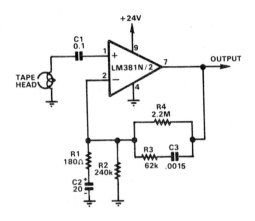

Figure 46 Tape playback amplifier using the LM381N

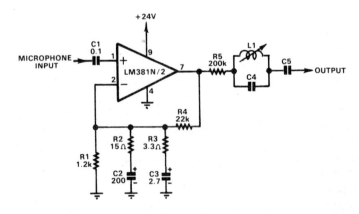

Figure 47 Tape recording preamplifier; the other channel is identical to the circuit shown

Recording preamplifier

A tape recording preamplifier using the LM381N is shown in Fig. 47. Frequency selective feedback is again used to obtain a suitable overall frequency response.

The resistors R4 and R1 determine the gain at very low frequencies (below the audio range) and therefore set the bias and the mean potential at the output of the amplifier. The components R2 and C2 become effective at audio frequencies and set the audio gain at low and medium frequencies, whilst C3 and R3 set the gain at high audio frequencies.

The components L1 and C4 resonate at the tape recorder oscillator bias frequency and form a 'bias trap' which greatly reduces the high frequency bias level at the output of the LM381N.

Magnetic cartridge circuit

Crystal and ceramic cartridges provide output signals of amplitudes 0.1 V to 2 V and no preamplifier is usually required (see, for example, the circuit of Fig. 40 in Chapter 6). However, magnetic record player cartridges produce outputs of only a few mV and a preamplifier is essential. This preamplifier must not only provide the required gain, but must also have the normal RIAA (Record Industry Association of America) playback equalisation characteristic which is used by virtually all recording companies.

A complete preamplifier with tone controls for use with a magnetic cartridge is shown in Fig. 48. The signal from the magnetic cartridge is first amplified by the LM381N stage; this brings the signal up to such an amplitude that any noise introduced into the circuit at a later stage will be small compared with the signal level. The amplifier stage also isolates the input from the following volume and tone control circuits.

The capacitors C3 and C4 in the LM381N feedback network provide the required RIAA characteristic by frequency selective negative feedback. Four variable resistors provide the controls required in the one channel of the stereo system, but the balance control R11 is common to both channels. If a monaural system is required, R11 may be completely omitted.

One normally wishes to make the same alteration to the volume, treble or bass in each channel at any time. Each of these controls should therefore normally consist of a two-gang variable resistor, each section

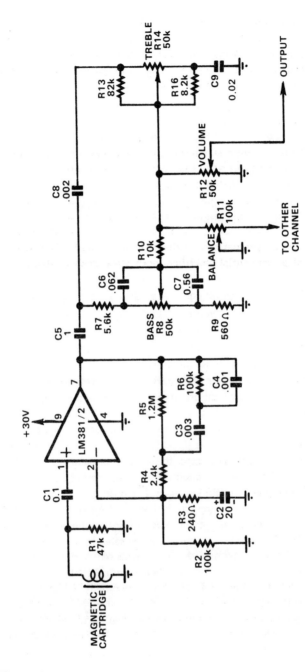

Figure 48 Complete magnetic cartridge amplifier with the RIAA response using the LM381N which is coupled by C5 to the tone control circuit shown on the right

having the value shown, one section being used in each of the two channels. As in all audio equipment, it is advantageous to use a potentiometer with a logarithmic response for the volume control so that the volume appears to change fairly uniformly to the human ear which has a response which is approximately logarithmic.

The LM387N

The LM387N has an internal circuit which is similar to that of the LM381N, but is encapsulated in the smaller 8 pin dual-in-line case as opposed to the 14 pin dual-in-line package used for the LM381N. Fewer connecting pins are available in the LM387N and it can be used only with a differential input stage, whereas the LM381N can be used with its input stage operating in the single ended mode for minimum noise or alternatively in the differential mode. The two transistors of a differential amplifier input stage both contribute to the noise.

The LM387N does not have connections for an external capacitor which may be required for stability when the gain is less than 10.

The LM382N

The LM382N is another device like the LN381N from the same manufacturer, but the LM382N has internal resistors connected so that the

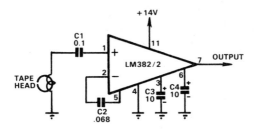

Figure 49 Simple LM382N tape playback circuit

number of external components required in tape recorders and in record players is minimised. The LM382N is encapsulated in a 14 pin dual-in-line package, but no facilities are provided for single ended operation or for additional frequency compensation at low values of gain.

A simple circuit using the LM382N as a tape recorder preamplifier is shown in Fig. 49. It may be compared with the slightly more complex circuit of Fig. 46 using the LM381N.

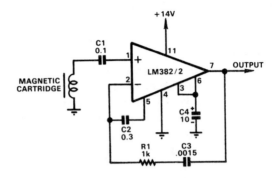

Figure 50 Simple LM382N record player amplifier for use with a magnetic cartridge

An LM382N preamplifier for use with a magnetic cartridge is shown in Fig. 50. It provides RIAA equalisation and may be compared with the part of the Fig. 48 circuit on the left hand side of C5. The output from the circuit of Fig. 49 or Fig. 50 may be fed via a 1 μF coupling capacitor to a tone and volume control circuit similar to that shown in Fig. 48.

The LM382N and LM387N have a hum rejection figure quoted as 110 dB to 120 dB. This is a very high value and is a valuable feature in low noise, low level circuits.

The MC1339P

The Motorola MC1339P is another dual stereo preamplifier device which has a built-in 7.5 V regulator and emitter follower outputs. It has a 16 V maximum power supply rating as opposed to the 40 V ratings of the National Semiconductor devices.

A simple magnetic cartridge preamplifier using the MC1339P is shown in Fig. 51. RIAA equalisation is, of course, provided by the components in the negative feedback network. Tape replay and recording amplifiers have also been published using this device.

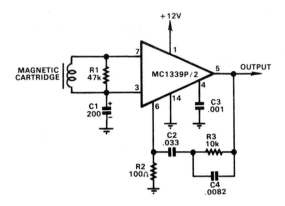

Figure 51 Record player amplifier using the MC1339P

Motorola also still offer their earlier MC1303L dual stereo preamplifier device.

The µA739 and the TB231

The Fairchild µA739 is equivalent to the SGS-ATES TBA231 dual low noise operational amplifier. These 14 pin dual-in-line devices require external frequency compensation, so they require a few more external components than the devices already discussed. However, they can be employed in the same general type of circuits as those shown in this chapter for other devices.

The Fairchild µA749 is similar to the µA739, but has an 'uncommitted collector' output. This means that the collector of the output stage is connected only to the output pin, whereas in the µA739 there is an internal 5 kΩ load resistor.

The ZN424

The ZN424 is a Ferranti device which is available in 14 pin and 8 pin dual-in-line packages and also in a circular metal TO-39 encapsulation. It is a development of the earlier ZN402 device and can be used in the same circuits. Unlike the devices discussed previously, only one amplifier is incorporated in each ZN424 package, but the ZN424 has a gating

73

facility which disconnects the output from the input when the gating connection is grounded. This gating facility makes multiplex operation possible; that is, the device may be used as a switch so that several signals can be successfully transmitted along a single channel.

The ZN424 employs a Class A output stage for minimum distortion and produces very low noise. A simple, high performance non-inverting amplifier with a gain of 100 is shown in Fig. 52. The cut off frequency

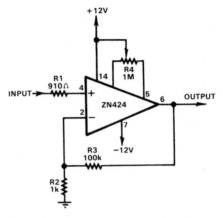

Figure 52 ZN424 amplifier with a gain of 100

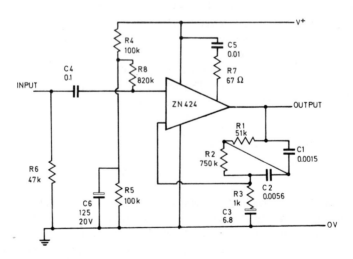

Figure 53 ZN424 circuit for use with a magnetic cartridge

74

is about 2 MHz and the slew rate about 20 V/μs, whilst the input impedance is about 10 MΩ in parallel with 2 pF. The total harmonic distortion at 1 kHz and 12 V peak-to-peak output is typically 0.1%.

A Magnetic cartridge preamplifier using the ZN424 is shown in Fig. 53. This provides the normal RIAA characteristic by means of the components in the negative feedback loop. The voltage gain at 1 kHz has been fixed at 50 (34 dB), since the output is then of a suitable amplitude for feeding to most power amplifiers.

The circuit of Fig. 53 provides very low distortion. The open loop distortion is typically 1.5% at an output peak voltage swing of 2 V. The open loop gain is about 20 000 (86 dB), so the feedback in the circuit shown is 86 dB − 34 dB = 52 dB and this reduces the distortion from 1.5% to 0.004%. More gain may be obtained by reducing R3, but C3 must then be increased in proportion to avoid loss of bass.

The components C3 and R3 provide an effective rumble filter, whilst C5 and R7 provide for stability at all supply voltages. The signal to noise ratio is better than 70 dB below an input level of 5 mV. The overload factor is about 40 dB referred to a 5 mV input with a 30 V supply.

The ZN459

The circuits discussed previously in this Chapter introduce relatively little noise, but their noise is nevertheless greater than that of the best available circuits employing discrete components. However, Ferranti introduced their ZN459 low noise wideband preamplifier device in

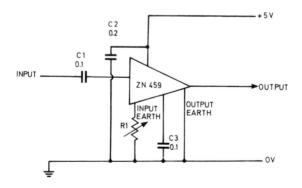

Figure 54 Circuit using the ZN459 ultra-low noise amplifier

75

1977; this can provide a noise level comparable with that of the best discrete circuits, but with the normal advantages one obtains by using an integrated circuit. The ZN459 is available in an 8 pin dual-in-line package as the ZN459CP and in circular metal packages with 6 leads as the ZN459CT and the wide temperature range ZN459T.

The ZN459 may be used in the type of circuit shown in Fig. 54. It is important to note that the absolute maximum permissible supply voltage is 6 V. The current taken from the power supply line is only 2 to 3 mA at 5 V. There is an internal feedback loop decoupled by C2 and this component should be directly connected to the input earth if R1 is zero or to the one end of R1. The value of R1 alters the amount of feedback and therefore the gain. If R1 is zero, the gain of the circuit is 1000 (60 dB), falling to 100 (40 dB) when R1 is 470 Ω. Increasing R1 increases the input impedance at the expense of noise.

The noise from the ZN459 device is equivalent to the random noise in a resistor of only 40 Ω connected across the input. This device provides a 15 MHz typical bandwidth, whilst the total harmonic distortion is 0.15%. The supply rejection ratio is 42.5 dB.

Appendix
Glossary of Terms

Active filter. An active filter employs some form of active device (often an operational amplifier) in a circuit which filters out certain frequencies or bands of frequencies. The filtering components are usually resistors and capacitors in the feedback network.

Analogue device. Analogue devices are employed in linear circuits in which the signal amplitude is analogous to a physical quantity. For example, in an audio amplifier, the signal level is related to the sound intensity.

Bandwidth. The gain of an operational amplifier falls with frequency. The bandwidth is the frequency at which the gain has fallen by 3 dB or a factor of $1/\sqrt{2}$, with reference to the low frequency gain.

BiFET Devices. BiFET devices contain two junction field effect transistors in their input stages which are fabricated on the same silicon chip as the bipolar transistors used in the other parts of the device. Initially BiFET devices were only operational amplifiers, but now the BiFET process is also employed for the fabrication of other devices.

BiMOS Devices. BiMOS devices contain Metal-Oxide-Silicon (MOS) transistors fabricated on the same silicon chip as the bipolar devices used in the other parts of the device. BiMOS operational amplifiers have a very high input impedance.

Channel separation. If a signal is applied at the input of one amplifier of a device containing more than one amplifier, the signal will appear at very low levels at the other outputs. The channel separation is the ratio of the signal at the desired output to that at any other output; it is normally expressed in dB.

Chip. A term commonly used to signify an integrated circuit, but one which should really be used for the silicon on which an IC or other solid state device is fabricated.

Closed loop gain. The gain of an operational amplifier circuit with negative feedback applied (that is, with the negative feedback loop closed).

Common mode. An input signal applied to both the inverting and non-inverting inputs simultaneously is known as a common mode signal.

Common mode rejection ratio. The common mode rejection ratio is a measure of the ability of an amplifier to reject signals applied to both the inverting and non-inverting inputs. It is equal to the gain with a signal applied to only one input divided by the gain with the signal applied to both inputs.

Comparator. An operational amplifier used as a comparator compares the input signal voltages at its inverting and non-inverting inputs. The output from the comparator is either 'high or 'low' depending on which of the input voltages is higher. Although almost any operational amplifier can be used as a comparator, amplifiers especially designed for use as comparators are available which switch very rapidly from one output state to the other.

Current differencing amplifier. A current differencing amplifier is rather like an operational amplifier, but the output is dependent on the difference between two input currents rather than the difference between two input voltages. Very cheap quad current differencing amplifiers are available.

Differential voltage gain. The differential voltage gain of an operational amplifier is the ratio of the change in the output voltage to the small change in the input voltage producing it. (See also **Closed loop gain** and **Open loop gain**).

Dual amplifier. A dual amplifier contains two separate amplifiers in a single package.

Dual-in-line. Dual-in-line devices have two rows of connecting pins, one on each side of the body of the device.

FET input operational amplifier. An operational amplifier which employs one or more field effect transistors in the input stage. One of the main advantages is that of very high input impedance.

Frequency compensation. An operational amplifier would oscillate at high frequencies if one or more internal or external frequency compensating components were omitted.

Gain. The gain of an amplifier is normally the voltage gain which is the change in the output voltage divided by the change in the input voltage which produced it. Both of these changes should be small. (See also **Closed loop gain** and **Open loop gain**.)

Heat sink. A piece of shaped metal connected to a power integrated circuit, or other solid state device, which can pass heat from the device to the surrounding air.

Input bias current. The average of the two currents to the inputs of an operational amplifier with no input signal applied.

Input offset current. The difference in the currents passing to the two inputs of an operational amplifier, when the output voltage is zero.

Input offset voltage. The difference in the voltages which must be applied to the two inputs of an operational amplifier in order to obtain an output voltage of zero. The voltages should be applied through two input resistors of equal value.

Input resistance. The resistance looking into either of the input terminals with the other input terminal grounded.

Input voltage range. The range of input voltages over which an amplifier will operate within its specifications and without damage to the amplifier.

Internal compensation. An amplifier with internal frequency compensation contains a capacitor fabricated on the silicon chip which enables the device to operate in a stable mode without oscillation, possibly under certain stipulated conditions.

Inverting input. A signal applied to the inverting input of an operational amplifier will produce an output signal of the opposite polarity.

Linear device. A device for use in a circuit in which the output voltage or current is linearly dependent on the input voltage or current. An operational amplifier is a linear device.

Logarithmic amplifier. The output from a logarithmic amplifier is proportional to the logarithm of the input voltage. A circuit of this type usually employs an operational amplifier with a transistor in the negative feedback network. A large range of input signal amplitudes can be compressed into a small range of output amplitudes.

Maximum power dissipation. The maximum power dissipation of a device is the maximum power which can be dissipated within that device and yet allow it to continue to operate within the manufacturer's specification and without damage.

Microcircuit. A microcircuit is an integrated circuit.

Monolithic devices. A monolithic device is one fabricated on a single chip of silicon or, in other words, an integrated circuit.

MOS device. An MOS device employs Metal-Oxide-Silicon FETs. In operational amplifiers these offer very high input impedance, as in the RCA CA3130 and CA3140 devices.

Non-inverting input. A signal applied to the non-inverting input of an operational amplifier will produce an output signal of the same polarity as the input.

Offset nulling. Offset nulling is the adjustment of an external variable resistor in an operational amplifier circuit so that the output voltage is made zero when both input potentials are zero.

79

Open loop gain. The open loop gain of an operational amplifier is the gain without feedback; that is, the gain with the feedback loop open circuit. This gain is normally very high indeed.

Operational amplifier. A high gain linear amplifier with inverting and non-inverting inputs.

Output offset voltage. The output voltage of the amplifier with respect to ground potential when both of the inputs are grounded.

Output resistance. The resistance seen looking into the output terminal with the output voltage at zero.

Output voltage swing. The peak output voltage swing which can be obtained from an amplifier without any appreciable clipping of the peaks of the waveform.

Power amplifier. An amplifier which can deliver a relatively large current and which can often operate from fairly high voltages. Power amplifiers are widely used in the audio field, but can also be used to drive servo motors, etc.

Power consumption. The power supplied as a direct current which is required to operate an amplifier with the output voltage at zero and no current passing through the load.

Power driver. A power driver is an amplifier with two outputs which can be used to drive a pair of complementary power transistors. The output power available from these transistors can be very high. An ordinary operational amplifier is not very suitable for use as a power driver, since only one output is available and this cannot be used easily to drive a pair of external power transistors which require a bias difference between their inputs for low cross-over distortion.

Programmable operational amplifier. An operational amplifier in which some of the parameters (such as input bias current, slew rate, power consumption, noise, etc.) can be set by means of an external resistor.

Quad amplifier. A quad amplifier contains four separate amplifiers in a single package.

Quiescent current. The quiescent current is the current taken from the power supply by an operational amplifier when no signal is applied to it and when no output current is being delivered.

Ripple rejection. The ratio of the peak-to-peak ripple voltage on the power supply line to the peak-to-peak ripple voltage at the output when no input is applied. The ripple rejection can often be increased by means of an additional by-passing capacitor, in which case it will vary with frequency.

Settling time. The settling time of an operational amplifier is the time delay between the application of a very quickly rising pulse at the input and the time when the output potential has settled to within a specified amount of its final value.

Short circuit current limit. In a device with short circuit current limiting, the output current is automatically limited by the internal circuit of the device to a value which will not cause damage to the device. It is normally found in power amplifiers and regulators designed to deliver high or fairly high power outputs.

Slew rate. The maximum rate at which a large change of output voltage can occur is known as the slew rate; it is normally measured in V/μs. It is quite different from bandwidth and only applies to signals producing a large output.

Supply voltage rejection ratio. The ratio of the change in the input offset voltage to the change in the supply voltage producing it.

Thermal overload protection. Many power devices include internal circuits which reduce the output current when the temperature of the silicon chip approaches the danger level. Nevertheless, such devices should not be allowed to become so hot that this protection circuitry operates for an appreciable time.

Thermal shutdown. See **Thermal overload protection.**

Transient response. The closed loop response of an amplifier to a sudden change in the input voltage (a 'step' function). Both the input and output voltage changes should be small so that small signal conditions apply.

Video amplifier. A wide bandwidth amplifier. The name comes from its possible use in television receiver video circuits.

Virtual ground. In some circuits an input of an operational amplifier remains almost at ground potential as the input signal changes; this point is said to be a virtual ground or virtual earth point.

Voltage follower. A circuit in which the output voltage closely follows the input voltage. It is normally an operational amplifier circuit with 100% negative feedback from the output to the inverting input.

Index of Devices

Index